NEST OF SPIES

Under the hot, mid-July sun, two men meet secretly at the sacred rock of the Acropolis in Athens. One of the men is Stephen Fletcher, alias Stefan Fettos, a British spy, the other is Colonel Spencer, Director of British Intelligence for the Balkans. At the meeting Fletcher learns that certain diplomatic moves, initiated by the British Government to bring about a settlement of the dispute between Greece and Turkey, are in danger of being sabotaged.

NEST OF SPIES

NEST OF SPIES

by

Geoffrey Davison

Magna Large Print Books
Long Preston, North Yorkshire,
BD23 4ND, England.

British Library Cataloguing in Publication Data.

Davison, Geoffrey
    Nest of spies.

    A catalogue record of this book is
    available from the British Library

    ISBN   978-0-7505-3653-0

First published in Great Britain in 1968 by Robert Hale Limited

Cover illustration © Daniela Lombard by arrangement with
Arcangel Images

Published in Large Print 2012 by arrangement with
Geoffrey Davison, care of Watson, Little Ltd.

Magna Large Print is an imprint of Library Magna Books Ltd.

Printed and bound in Great Britain by
T.J. (International) Ltd., Cornwall, PL28 8RW

To Gary

CHAPTER ONE

Two men made their way, independently, through the city of Athens, under the blistering hot, mid-July sun, towards the sacred rock of the Acropolis. They went, not with the intention of absorbing the atmosphere of ancient Greece, but to meet in secrecy for a few minutes to discuss a matter pertinent to the interests of the British Government.

One of these men was Colonel John Spencer, Director of British Intelligence for the Balkans, the other was Stephen Fletcher, alias Stefan Fettos, a British spy.

Spencer was an elderly man with the appearance and manner of a 'blimp'. He was of medium height, overweight, with a clipped military accent and a gruff manner. But beneath this pompous and rather outdated appearance was a very astute and orderly brain, with an expert's knowledge of the Balkans and the Middle East.

Spencer travelled by car, together with a small party who had joined Professor Kay, from Cambridge, on his last visit to the great treasure of antiquity before he boarded his boat for home. Spencer and his wife accompanied the Professor's party at the request of the Ambassador, but Spencer intended to turn the sightseeing trip to his own advantage.

Fletcher's mode of travel was entirely different from Spencer's. He made his way by train and bus. He had come from the busy port of Piraeus, where he lived and operated from a fishing smack at present anchored in the crowded harbour.

Fletcher was a much younger man than Spencer and, unlike Spencer, had known no other occupation than that of a spy. His ancestors on his mother's side were Greek, on his father's – Scots. He was born in Greece and had spent his childhood and youth in the consulates of the Balkan countries. At the age of eighteen he had been sent by the Foreign Office to Ankara University to study languages, and since that day had been on their payroll. In looks he was quite handsome with a strong face, dark hair and steel blue eyes. He was much taller than the average Greek, and had a deep resonant voice and confident manner. He accepted his way of life as part of his destiny. The Balkans were his home and his own particular responsibility. He moved freely through the various countries as if boundaries did not exist, and his contacts were many and varied. Whereas Spencer maintained a chain of contacts at attaché-and-Government level, Fletcher's net was spread over a broader cross-section of the population. But he did not work entirely on his own. His boat was too big for one man to handle, so he had a partner – a tough, hard bitten Greek mercenary, whose only loyalty was to Fletcher and whose knowledge of the cesspits of the many ports often proved invaluable.

It is not surprising that such men were present in Athens and Piraeus. All capitals have spies, and the eastern countries of the Mediterranean have been Britain's own special concern ever since it became part of her lifeline. But the volume and intensity of their work had greatly increased when the smouldering feud which existed between the Greeks and the Turks erupted to the surface over the Cyprus dispute.

Immediately the island became a flash point area it attracted the full attention of the Communist countries, and Athens and Piraeus took over the mantle once worn by Istanbul, Prague, Berlin and Paris. British Intelligence had not only the Greeks and Turks to content with, but also a very active organisation of Communist agents whose one aim was to keep the pot boiling and prevent a settlement.

On the 15th February, 1964 Britain brought the Cyprus dispute to the United Nations Security Council, and on the 4th March of the same year it was decided to

11

send a peace force to the island. An uncanny silence has since hung over the island – but not elsewhere. In the stately rooms of the diplomats and the backrooms of the spies, the battle has continued. For the physical eruption of force on the island of Cyprus was only the safety valve to a much deeper conflict between Greece and Turkey, the roots of which can only be found in the pages of history. Cyprus became a pawn in this dispute, with the Greeks determined to encourage a policy leading to 'enosis', and the Turks equally determined to have part of the island for their own people.

To the members of the N.A.T.O. alliance this unsettled part of the continent was a weakness, the feuding and military confront-ations an embarrassment. To the Commun-ists it was a chink in N.A.T.O.'s armour and, therefore, a situation to be exploited. To Britain, in particular, the situation was be-coming a constant source of concern and a threat to her economy. Besides the increasing financial burden of maintaining a military and naval force within the area, the threat of open conflict was perilously close to the oil fields of the Middle East, and the whole of the Middle East has explosive potentials which a stray spark could easily ignite.

When France first intimated her intentions to break with N.A.T.O., the other member nations quickly closed their ranks, and the

British Government was asked to mediate between Greece and Turkey in order that the situation should not develop into another Achilles' heel. It was a task Britain had been pursuing since the outbreak of the Cyprus hostilities, but with the backing of her more powerful allies she gladly renewed her attempts to bring about a settlement. After a considerable amount of diplomatic activity and the passing of time, the two powers eventually agreed to attempt to resolve their differences. As the forerunner to a full-blooded Foreign Ministers' meeting, a pre-liminary conference was arranged to take place, secretly, on the island of Rhodes, at which minor officials would prepare the way.

The importance to Britain of a successful outcome to this conference had been passed to Spencer and Fletcher in no uncertain terms. Nothing had to be allowed to rock the boat – nothing! But Spencer and Fletcher operated in a league in which the Communists, Greeks, and Turks, fielded their own teams and got their orders from their own Governments, and the natural desire for a country to produce an ace at the conference table meant a lot of activity for the spy. This conference was no exception as Spencer had learned, and he was in a hurry to start the counter moves.

When Fletcher arrived at the meeting place, Spencer and his party were already present. They were standing outside the Propylea listened to the Professor exalt the glory that was Greece. Fletcher slipped by, unnoticed by all but Spencer, and sat on a bench seat in the shade, and admired the plain of Attica which lay before him.

Spencer listened patiently to the Professor, but when the party started to move towards the Temple of Wingless Victory he turned to his wife and said: 'You go with the Professor, dear. I think I will have a rest.'

His wife looked at him concerned.

'Oh! dear!' she said. 'I do hope you are not getting another attack of malaria.'

Spencer hastened to assure her that it was nothing like that.

'Just this damned heat,' he muttered. 'It gets so hot.'

He gave her a gentle push and she rejoined the group. For a moment Spencer stood where he was, mopping his brow and having a last minute check that no furtive eyes were watching his movements.

When he joined Fletcher, he still had his handkerchief in his hand.

'This damned heat,' he muttered. 'God! It's a hot summer.'

Fletcher, who was seated at the other end of the bench from Spencer, looked straight ahead of him.

'You ought to have a spell in England,' he said.

14

'No good, old man,' Spencer replied, 'the cold would kill me.'

Fletched smiled at Spencer's somewhat paradoxical remark, but he sympathised with the man. For, like Spencer, he often longed to get away from the stifling heat, knowing only too well that he had lived too long in the hot climate to take kindly to a cooler atmosphere.

Spencer looked across the plain to the blue Mediterranean Sea.

'There's trouble brewing,' he said quietly.

Fletcher sighed, but he was not unduly surprised.

'What?' he asked.

'I wish I damned well knew,' Spencer growled, 'but I can feel it. Those blighters in the Greek Foreign Office are being a little too co-operative for my liking, and we haven't heard a squeak from the Turkish Embassy for nearly two weeks now.'

But Fletcher knew Spencer hadn't got him there just to listen to his fears.

'We've heard from Ankara,' Spencer added. 'That damned man Abdul Rassitz, has left Turkey, so no doubt we can expect him to be stirring up trouble soon.'

Fletcher gave an appreciative whistle. He could understand Spencer's concern now. Rassitz was a fanatic, a Turk who saw himself as the counterpart to Grivas and the saviour of the Turkish Cypriots, and like all rabble rousers he had his followers. His presence in the area could only spell trouble, and that was something they didn't want at that precise moment.

'I thought the Turkish Government had agreed to keep him under lock and key until after the conference,' he said.

'So they did, Fletcher,' Spencer agreed. 'No doubt they will give a plausible excuse for his escape, but you know what goes on before these conferences take place. We'll hear all about what Rassitz has been up to at the conference table – unless you find out before.'

Fletcher turned his back on Spencer. There was always a flurry of activity before any conference, but Rassitz could upset the conference altogether if he was played out of turn.

'Anything else?' he asked.

'Yes,' Spencer replied. 'Does the name Lofer mean anything to you?'

Lofer! Fletcher mentally wrestled with the name, but it did not register.

''Fraid not,' he muttered. 'Why?'

Spencer wiped his brow again.

'Pity,' he said. 'It came my way in the form of a diplomatic whisper, if you know what I mean.'

Fletcher knew what he meant all right. He knew they exchanged favours and passed information in the same way as Fletcher's underworld. Only they liked to embroider their actions in more delicate and subtle terms.

Spencer produced three photographs from his pocket and placed them on the seat alongside him. Fletcher deftly picked them up and with his back still to Spencer looked at each one in turn. The first photograph he looked at was of Rassitz, the Turk. It was an old photograph, but it nevertheless showed the man's deep-set dark eyes and his leathery-looking face with a duelling scar over his upper lip. He wasn't a pleasant man in person and his photograph did not hide the fact. The next photograph was also of a man, but a much younger man with a lean sallow face, dark hair and a neat, thin, black moustache. His eyes were much softer than those of Rassitz and he had the look of an intellectual. Fletcher placed him as a Turk, but he could have belonged to any of the Eastern Balkan countries. The last photograph was of a woman, a very attractive woman. She bore a remarkable resemblance to the man in the photograph Fletcher had just studied, but her face looked more determined, more sure of herself. It could have graced the cover of any beauty magazine. She had the classical high cheek bones, a full mouth with a flashing smile, dark eyes and long dark hair. A combination of eastern beauty with western sophistication. It was a face he would not forget. He didn't even attempt to give her an age. She was a woman and in their part of the world that meant anything from sixteen upwards. He replaced the photographs on the seat for Spencer to pick up.

'I recognise Rassitz,' he said, 'but who are the other two?'

'Kasim and Karima Mohmad,' Spencer explained. 'Recent additions to the Turkish Embassy. That place is slowly become another Trojan horse.'

'Brother and sister?' Fletcher asked.

'Yes.'

'Turkish-Cypriots or Turks?'

Spencer made a gesture with his hands which meant he didn't know.

'What do you want me to do?' Fletcher asked.

Spencer sighed.

'Anything,' he said, 'so long as you get an answer. If there is something being hatched up, we must know about it.'

'Give me twenty-four hours,' Fletcher whispered. 'I'll contact you.'

'You could always try that man Zonakas,' Spencer muttered.

'True,' Fletcher said, 'but if the Greek Government is involved we'll get nothing out of him.'

Spencer stood up.

'I'll leave it with you,' he said. 'Now where

the devil is the Professor?'

'They are just leaving the Temple,' Fletcher said, and glanced across at the Professor's party. He knew all of the people with the Professor except one – a small man with a neat, pointed, grey beard.

'Who is that small man with the beard?' he asked quickly.

'Dr Sleitser,' Spencer said. 'A German archaeologist. I believe he is working on some ancient temple on one of the islands. I'll be glad when we get the Professor on his blasted boat. All this mumbo jumbo about ancient Greece leaves me cold.' He gave a deep, rumbling laugh, as if he had thought of something amusing, and walked slowly away from the seat. When he rejoined the party his wife came up to him.

'Were you speaking to that Greek, John, dear?' she asked.

Spencer glowered at her.

'Of course not, Clara,' he replied gruffly. 'Why the devil should I be doing that?'

'Sorry, dear,' his wife said nervously. 'I thought I saw you talking to him, that was all.' She beat a hasty retreat and gave her full attention to the Professor.

Fletcher allowed a few minutes to elapse before leaving the Acropolis to return to Piraeus. As he joined the queue for the bus to take him to the station no one would have guessed his real occupation. Being a spy in a foreign country, it didn't pay to advertise, so Fletcher hid his identity by becoming part of the everyday scene. In appearance he looked like thousands of other Greeks, and the only clue that he was something other than one of the masses could have been obtained by watching his eyes, which furtively took in all that was happening and missed nothing. On this occasion Fletcher was also pensive. If there was trouble brewing it was his job to flush it out. But he had learned from past experience that there were no short cuts. It would take time, patience, and a lot of hard work.

From the station in Piraeus he weaved his way through the busy streets until he reached the south harbour, where he patiently sat in the shade of a dockside building watching the numerous ferry boats come and go. When the S.S. *Thasos* nosed its way into the harbour, he became more alert. Still without moving his position he watched the ferry come alongside and saw the passengers start to disembark. He gave a grunt of approval when he saw a small, dark, swarthy man come ashore, carrying a duffel bag flung over his shoulder. He looked older than Fletcher, but had an alert face and flashing eyes. His chest and biceps filled his shirt to its full extent and gave him the appearance of being a man not to be crossed or taken lightly.

As the man left the boat, Fletcher also left

his cool vantage point and walked slowly away from the jetty. Without waiting to see if the man was following him, he left the harbour for one of the many back streets which ran parallel with the front. Increasing his speed, he slipped through the rows of white buildings into a narrow side street and entered an obscure little bar, well hidden from the everyday tourist. The only occupant in the room was Nico, the proprietor, and immediately Fletcher entered the bar, Nico eased his sixteen stone off his stool and slid a bottle of local brandy across the counter. Fletcher collected the bottle and took a seat away from the counter, close to the single fan which fought an endless battle with the smoke and heat.

A few seconds later the man from the boat entered the bar. He nodded his head in recognition to Nico and walked over and sat opposite Fletcher. For a second the two men looked at each other, and then exchanged greetings in a manner which left no doubt as to the respect and feeling they had for each other. They were, in fact, partners. Stephen Fletcher, the British spy, and Mario Fuigelo, professional murderer, gun runner, smuggler and free-lance mercenary. But they were only partners when it suited each other's purpose. Fletcher had only one master whereas Mario was prepared to do business with whoever paid his price – so long as business did not clash with Fletcher's interests.

'Your business was successful?' Fletcher asked.

Mario grinned – a broad friendly grin which lit up his whole face.

'Stefan,' he said slapping Fletcher on the shoulder, 'I told you it was not business on this occasion, but pleasure.' He kissed the air. 'Great pleasure!' He came closer and whispered secretly: 'There is a small island south of Santorini where the beauty of the scenery is only matched by the local girls who run naked through the woods. That is where I go, Stefan – to rest.' He gave a long deep laugh. 'I have to pay them a call to keep them happy.' He slapped Fletcher again. 'But I do not want to overstay my welcome.'

Fletcher warmed to his exuberance.

'You and your mythical island,' he said.

Mario preened himself.

'I tell you this is no myth, my friend. One day I will take you and you will see for yourself.'

Fletcher smiled. Perhaps there was a half truth in what Mario said. Perhaps one day he would even go with him. But there were more urgent matters at the moment.

'There's trouble brewing,' he said quietly.

Mario swore. 'This is the height of the summer,' he grumbled. 'It is too hot for trouble.'

'Rassitz has left Turkey.'

Mario swore again. He didn't like Rassitz, but then he was a Greek and he didn't like many Turks.

'What else?' he asked.

'Does the name Lofer mean anything to you?'

Mario shook his head.

'Didn't think it would,' Fletcher muttered. 'They want us to stir it up a little and see what comes to the surface.'

Mario sighed.

'I suppose that is what we are paid to do,' he said. 'When do we start?'

'Straight away. The *Tonos* is in its usual berth at the north end of the harbour. Put your gear aboard and take the harbour area. I will go into Athens. We will meet on the boat.'

'The afternoon is time for siesta, not work,' Mario said thoughtfully, 'and all my friends prefer it that way.'

'In that case, Mario, you had better catch them before they leave the bars for their woman and their beds.'

Mario grunted and sank his drink. He picked up his duffel bag and slipped silently out of the bar.

Fletcher followed him, but before leaving he put Nico in the picture so that he could handle any callers.

Fletcher and Mario had their own contacts

23

and their own way of doing business. Mario's contacts were in the underworld and vice gangs which gather around any seaport like wasps around a honey pot. Men who would perform any task and not ask questions, so long as they got paid.

Fletcher's contacts fell into two categories. Those who worked for him alone, and those who supplied information as a commodity in a competitive market. Nico fell into the first category. So did Toni who operated a taxi in Athens, and Miguel, the hairdresser, whose shop was opposite the Government buildings, and Gina, secretary to Doctor Astoros, a member of the Greek cabinet. So also was Patriarch Father Peikos, and there were others.

In the second category were a host of small syndicates which had mushroomed and flourished as the work of the spy had increased in intensity. They existed in the customs offices, in the shipping offices, the post office, the civil service and even the police. They made the work of the spy easier and his expense account greater.

After leaving Nico's bar, Fletcher quickly set the wheels in motion in Piraeus. He didn't wait for results. He was prepared to buy and if there was a seller they knew where to contact him. From Piraeus he went by train into Athens, collected Toni at his stand outside the station, and started a quick tour of the capital which began at the airport, but which took him to many surprising and unusual places. As the afternoon wore on, however, it became obvious that the market was dead. If something big was being hatched it was still in the nest. Finally, as a last resort before leaving the capital, he decided to come out into the open and visit a man who operated at the same level as himself, Andros Zonakas.

Zonakas was a Greek, who ran an unofficial network for his Government, independent of Greek Security. Fletcher kept himself well informed of Zonakas' movements, as he did also with Veti, the Communist. But whereas Veti was the opposition, Zonakas could be friend or foe dependent upon the play that was being made. Fletcher didn't like the man, nor did he trust him, but on occasions it suited his purpose to do business with him. This was one of the occasions.

Zonakas lived in a fashionable district on a wooded slope, several kilometres north of the city, in splendid isolation. But not so isolated for him not to have visitors. As they manipulated the sharp bend and entered the cul-de-sac of luxury apartments where he lived, a man came hurrying along the pavement towards them.

'Kronos,' Toni muttered from behind the steering-wheel.

Fletcher sat up and looked at the man.

'Dimitri Kronos?' he asked.

'Yes.'

Fletcher had heard of him. He was one of the many small fish who swam with the sharks and fed on their left overs. In stature, strangely enough, Kronos was also small, but he had a friendly face which was engulfed by a thick mass of jet black hair.

'That's interesting,' Fletcher said thoughtfully.

'He is certainly in a hurry,' Toni added.

Fletcher frowned. 'I hope Zonakas hasn't scurried away as well,' he muttered.

But Zonakas was receiving visitors, and Fletcher was ushered into the apartment by his servant. He was taken to a large room, decorated and furnished in garish colours. Zonakas was on his balcony, playfully caressing a bunch of grapes which hung from the vines he had cultivated. He had his back to Fletcher.

'Bring a carafe of wine, Zeus,' he said, without turning round. 'You know Mister Fettos' taste.' He spoke in a deep cultured voice which had only a slightly artificial ring about it.

He swung round and beamed at Fletcher.

'There! I am right. It is you, Stefan. I must be psychic.'

He was tall, like Fletcher, and also quite handsome, but his features had become soft with easy living. His mannerisms were slow, sophisticated and affected, and he had a

26

conceited air about him which could cause irritation.

He was smiling, benevolently, at Fletcher, displaying a beautiful array of pearl-white dentures.

'Not psychic,' Fletcher said, 'observant. Your balcony overlooks the road from the plain. You must have seen me arrive in my taxi.'

Zonakas looked hurt.

'There you go again, Stefan, trying to deflate my ego.'

He walked into the room and took off a smock he had been wearing to protect his expensive, colourful, silk shirt from the grapes.

'I saw Kronos as I arrived,' Fletcher said casually.

Zonakas looked surprised and then disinterested.

'Small fry,' he said. 'He must have other contacts in the area. Ah! Here is the wine. I think you will like this, Stefan. It has been a good year. This comes from my vineyard on Tinos.'

The boy filled the glasses and Fletcher admired the wine before referring back to Kronos.

'So Kronos has not been to see you,' he said.

Zonakas shook his head.

'No, not me,' he said firmly.

Fletcher didn't believe him.

'Everything is very quiet, then?'

'So it should be Stefan. It is summer, it is too hot.'

'But you are still in Athens, Andros, and that's what worries me.'

Zonakas laughed.

'You flatter me, Stefan, but to ease your mind let me tell you that I am off to Switzerland next week.'

'Why next week?'

'Because it suits my arrangements.'

Fletcher gave him a long, hard look.

'Andros,' he said quietly, 'what is going on?'

Zonakas looked surprised.

'My dear, Stefan, why should anything be going on?'

'Because there is a conference next month,' Fletcher said evenly.

'So?' Zonakas asked. 'My Government is supporting it.'

'Look, Andros,' Fletcher said with more feeling. 'I am no fool. Ever since the days you stopped believing in your ancient gods, your Government has never sat down at a conference table without having gone to great lengths to bend things their way. If this is going on I want to know about it.' He paused and then added: 'And if anyone is weaving the web it will be you, Andros!'

He didn't expect a confession out of Zonakas, but he had hoped to get something out of his reactions. However, he was disappointed. Zonakas only smiled blandly.

'My dear Stefan,' he said cheerfully. 'I like you. You pay me high compliments and you have noble intentions. I only wish we could do business as we have in the past, but,' he shrugged, 'I have nothing to sell and my holiday is approaching.'

'Being a noble gentleman, Andros, I know you wouldn't lie to me.' There was only the slightest trace of cynicism in Fletcher's voice. 'Because if I found out that you were stirring up trouble for my Government, I would finish you!'

The sting in the tail was no idle threat. Spencer could bring the right pressure to bear in the proper quarters. They would find a replacement, but Zonakas wouldn't enjoy his luxuries any longer.

Zonakas flushed up momentarily.

'For a man who poses as a Greek and whose background would not hold very close investigation by the authorities, you speak strong words,' he said.

'At least my background is legitimate,' Fletcher replied.

There was a short, delicate silence.

'Now you are trying to hurt me,' Zonakas said with forced lightness to ease the tension.

Fletcher ignored his remark.

'Are you sure you have nothing to tell me?'

he asked.

'I wish I had, Stefan,' Zonakas said regretfully. 'I do not like to see you like this, especially when you are worrying unnecessarily.'

Fletcher replaced his glass on the silver server.

'I hope you are right, Andros,' he said meaningly, and added casually: 'Have you heard that Rassitz has left Turkey?'

'I must confess I have,' Zonakas replied.

'And it doesn't worry you?'

'Not me,' Zonakas said. 'Perhaps my Government, but I am thinking only of my holidays.'

'Well, enjoy yourself, Andros, and if you haven't been telling me the truth I shouldn't hurry back.'

Zonakas smiled.

'I will see you in a few weeks,' he said. 'We must have dinner together.'

Fletcher walked to the entrance hall which adjoined the room in which they had been talking. The boy stood waiting for him, a white linen trilby in his hand.

'Your hat, Mr Fettos,' he said.

'I didn't have a hat,' Fletcher said, loud enough for Zonakas to hear. 'Perhaps Mr Kronos left it!'

He gave Zonakas one last look, saw the annoyance on his face, and left the apartment to rejoin Toni.

It hadn't been a wasted journey altogether, he thought, as they motored back to Piraeus. Kronos' hasty departure suggested that Zonakas was not being so idle as he had tried to imply, and if he was doing something the British Government wouldn't approve of he would now be having second thoughts. Zonakas had long since learned that Fletcher was not a man to be taken lightly.

On reaching the harbour Fletcher went straight to Nico's bar, but, as he had now come to anticipate, the information which had been channelled back to him was of little merit. But Fletcher was not finished yet. He had one more call to make before rejoining Mario, and that was to Father Peikos, Patriarch of the Byzantine church of Saint Peter in Piraeus. His friendship with the Patriarch was one which even Fletcher couldn't fully explain. He had been introduced to the man by his father, and from their very first encounter the Patriarch had proved a very valuable friend. Their friendship was a secret which Fletcher guarded jealously.

Inside the church he made his way to the altar and lit a candle. As a long-bearded priest walked slowly across the altar swinging incense about him, Fletcher sat patiently in a position of prayer and meditation. There were several other people in the church, and after performing his ceremony at the altar he took his place in one of the pews.

Several minutes later, a small, portly patriarch entered the church from one of the side doors. He went first to the altar and then to a small dark alcove at the side of the church. Fletcher quietly left his pew and joined him. The two men sat opposite each other. The Patriarch's face was hidden behind his fertile beard, but his eyes looked soft and friendly. Fletcher bowed his head, and the Patriarch mumbled a short blessing, moving his crucifix across Fletcher's body.

'Is something troubling you, my son?' he asked. There was a slight trace of a foreign accent in his voice.

'No, Father,' Fletcher replied, 'not me, but my friends are worried.'

Fletched looked up at the Patriarch's face, but got no encouragement. His eyes were closed.

'Carry on,' the Patriarch mumbled.

'My friends are under the impression that there is a party being organised for a guest from the east, and they are not going to be invited to attend.'

The Patriarch remained silent for a while.

'I know of no such party,' he said finally.

'It is being kept very quiet,' Fletcher sighed.

'Have your friends any information at all?'

'None,' Fletcher replied. 'Except the name of the guest.'

'Who is he?' the Patriarch asked.

'Abdul Rassitz,' Fletcher whispered.

There was a long pause.

'Yesterday, Dimitri Kronos came here to worship,' the Patriarch said very quietly. 'He was wearing an expensive suit. He put a lot of money into the poor box. It is not like him. Perhaps he can help you.'

Fletcher gave a satisfied grunt. The Patriarch didn't bandy names around lightly, and Kronos has been visiting Zonakas. It was a coincidence which deserved investigating.

'Thank you,' Fletcher said, 'I will talk to him. If you hear of the party, I would like to know of it.'

The Patriarch nodded his head.

'It shall be,' he muttered.

Fletcher left soon afterwards. He had got his starting point – Dimitri Kronos! He hurried through the labyrinth of narrow streets to the North Pier where the *Tonos* was moored, eager to start the wheels in motion.

Mario was already on board. He was lying on his bunk smoking a cigarillo. One look at his face and Fletcher knew he had drawn a blank.

'Nothing, Mario?' he said.

Mario shook his head.

'Not a bloody thing. How about you?'

'Dead duck,' Fletcher said, and paused. 'What do you know about Dimitri Kronos?'

Mario turned on his side to face him.

'He does a bit of smuggling and gun running,' he said. 'Buys and sells information.

Nothing big, but he gets by.'

'Any particular allegiance?' Fletcher asked.

'No. He is not interested in politics. Greek, Arab, Turk – it is all the same to him. He works for whoever pays him.'

'What about the Communists?'

'If it suits his purpose. I tell you, Stefan, he is all right.'

'Could you contact him?'

Mario's face lit up and he swung off his bunk.

'You know something, Stefan?' he asked eagerly.

'It may be nothing, Mario,' Fletcher said, 'but I saw Kronos this afternoon. He had been visiting Zonakas.'

'So?' Mario asked.

'I am also told that he has been giving an unusual display of wealth recently.'

Mario looked at him.

'He couldn't have got that from Zonakas,' he said. 'He pays very little.'

'Precisely,' Fletcher agreed. 'Kronos obviously has some other source.'

'And Zonakas?'

'I don't know, Mario. Perhaps Kronos is selling to him.'

Mario growled.

'In that case, the sooner we find out the better.'

He stamped out his cigarillo.

'What do you want me to do?' he asked.

'Arrange a meeting with him. We can afford to spend a few drachmas.'

'Tonight?' Mario asked.

'Yes,' Fletcher said, 'tonight.' The sooner the better, he thought. He didn't like this period of uncertainty. If something was going on he had to be in on it. Mario caught the urgency and left straight away.

Fletcher followed him on deck, and sat by the wheelhouse watching the crowds which thronged the illuminated harbour front. It was a ritual for them. In the cool of the evening they appeared like ants from their hill, and it had been particularly hot that day. He was still sitting on deck when Mario returned. Mario hadn't been able to contact Kronos personally, but had left a message for him to meet them later that evening in one of the bars that Kronos was known to use. Fletcher felt more relaxed. It was only a slim lead, but he knew Father Peikos well enough to suspect it had a deeper significance.

The bar in which the meeting had been arranged was no different from any of the other bars which fronted the harbour and dockyards, but it was in a quarter which Fletcher and Mario rarely visited. It was a long, rectangular-shaped room, drably furnished with a functional bar counter at one end. When Fletcher and Mario arrived the dimly lit room had acquired its customary haze of light blue smoke. As soon as they entered the room Fletcher had an uneasy feeling bout the place. It was unusually quiet despite the presence of a number of dockyard layabouts. Kronos was not yet present.

They sat at a corner table and ignored the hostile glances which came their way.

'Not a very friendly crowd,' Fletcher muttered.

Mario shrugged. 'This is not the Y.M.C.A.,' he said.

The bartender, a sullen looking Greek, came over to them and Mario ordered the drinks. Fletcher glanced at his watch. It was 10 p.m. The time they had arranged to meet Kronos.

An uncanny silence hung over the room.

'I don't like it, Mario,' Fletcher said finally. 'We'll give him another ten minutes.'

Mario moved his chair so that he was in a position to watch the other occupants. He also had a feeling about the place.

The bartender brought their drinks and they sat idly playing with the glasses. Fletcher was becoming restless. In their business, punctuality was one of the rules. He was on the verge of accepting that it had been a fruitless visit when a man appeared at the entrance door ... but it was not Kronos.

'I think we are about to have company,' Mario said quietly.

He was a tall, well-made man, in a

crumpled, white linen suit. He wore a white straw trilby hat. He was looking in their direction. Fletcher saw him glance at the bartender who gave a quick nod of his head.

'Police,' Mario grunted.

The man came over to them. He grabbed a chair, swung it around, and sat facing them with his arms resting on the chair back.

'You want something?' Mario growled.

The man ignored the question. He had a bulging pocket where he kept his armoury. His face looked hard and he reeked of garlic.

'What do you want with Kronos?' he asked.

'That's our business,' Mario snapped.

'And mine,' the man said. He produced a police identification card which showed his photograph. Underneath it was his name and rank, Detective Sergeant Nepolis.

The Sergeant repeated his question, but this time it was directed at Fletcher.

'It is a personal matter,' Fletcher said evenly.

'Tell me about it,' the Sergeant suggested in a supercilious manner.

Fletcher shrugged.

'He borrowed one thousand drachmas from me last year when we were fishing off Thira. Times are hard. I want it back.'

The Sergeant leered. 'You lent Kronos one thousand drachmas,' he scoffed.

'Is that a crime?' Mario asked.

The Sergeant looked stern.

'Let's go own to the station. You can tell your story to Inspector Ikarios.'

Fletcher's pulse quickened. The Sergeant's presence had been unexpected, but the name of the Inspector at the police station even more so. Fletcher knew of Ikarios. He wasn't a normal police inspector, he had other duties. He was part of Greek security!

'Will he give me my money back?' Fletcher asked, playing for time. If they were going in front of Ikarios they would have to get their story straight.

'It is most unlikely,' the Sergeant sneered, 'but he will be most interested to hear about it.'

'Then why don't you tell him for us?' Mario snorted. His contempt for the police was obvious.

Fletcher could see the limit of the Sergeant's patience had been reached. Quickly he intervened.

'Look, Sergeant, I don't know what this is all about,' he said. 'As I have told you, we met Kronos last year when we were fishing and taking tourists from Crete to Thira. Times were good. We met Kronos in a bar and I lent him the money. He wanted some money to take a party of tourists north to Lemnos. Now I want it back. That is all.' It was more for Mario's benefit than the Sergeant's.

The policemen stood up and moved his head to indicate they were to go with him.

'Don't let's have any bother,' he said, and slapped his bulging pocket to add weight to his remark. 'I have two men outside,' he added.

Mario exchanged glanced with Fletcher. If Fletcher wanted to mix it, all he had to do was give him the nod. But Fletcher didn't want this. They had thrown a few pebbles in the pool hoping for a ripple and they had got one. It hadn't been what they had expected, but the mere fact that Ikarios was involved meant they were fishing in the same pool. Fletcher wanted to see what developed.

He made a resigned gesture.

'Come, Mario,' he said. 'We weren't doing anything special this evening.'

They stood up and allowed the policeman to escort them out of the bar, Mario a little more reluctant than Fletcher. At the door, Mario hesitated and glanced at the bartender who had diplomatically refrained from charging them for their drinks. There was a depth of meaning in the look Mario gave him. One day he would be paid!

CHAPTER TWO

The Inspector was a small man, unusually small for a policeman, Fletcher thought, as he sat facing him in his office. He was not a likeable man. He had a ferret-like face with a narrow mouth and beady eyes. He sat slowly moving his chair around its pivot, with a cane fly swat in his hand. At the end of the cane was a bunch of thin leather strips, and occasionally the Inspector swished the air with a swift flashing movement as a fly came within his range. It was hot in the room, especially where Fletcher was sitting. The fan was directed towards the Inspector, whilst Fletcher received the full force of a powerful table-lamp. The perspiration began to flow down his brow. The Inspector took a long drink of cool water, but didn't offer Fletcher the same luxury.

'Name?' the Inspector barked in a high-pitched voice.

'Stefan Fettos,' Fletcher said.

'Nationality?'

'Greek.'

'By birth?'

'Yes.'

'Where were you born?'

'On Chios.'

'When?'

'February 9th, 1936.'

'And where do you live?'

'Same place.'

'Your parents still live there?'

'No. They are both dead. Why do you ask me these questions, Inspector? I told the Sergeant why we wanted to see Kronos. What have I done wrong?'

'This is what we want to find out,' the Inspector snapped.

Fletcher mentally sighed. The Inspector had nothing on him. He was playing with him, fishing around. But why? Why should Greek Security be so interested in Kronos? Why bring Fletcher in for cross examination just because he had arranged to meet him?

He resigned himself to further baiting. As a supposedly illiterate fisherman he had no alternative.

'What do you do for a living?'

'Fish.'

'Where?'

'Wherever there are fish. Occasionally off Salamis or around the islands.'

'But that is far from your home.'

'We move around in the summer. It is better that we fish near home in the winter. We also pick up some tourist business.'

The Inspector cracked his fly swat perilously close to Fletcher's face.

'Have you ever carried any cargo?'

'No, Inspector.'

This time the leather strips caught Fletcher's chin with a razor-like cut. Fletcher gritted his teeth.

'No guns?' the Inspector asked sarcastically.

'Guns?' Fletcher asked incredulously. 'Never. I am a fisherman, Inspector. You can search my boat. Ask the authorities on Chios. I assure you Inspector, I have never carried guns.'

'But you know Kronos carries guns?'

'No, Inspector. I do not. I would not have contacted him if I had known that.'

'When did you first meet him?'

'Last year on Thira. We met in a bar and we drank together. Times were good, there was a lot of tourist business. Kronos asked me to lend him a thousand drachmas and like a fool I did.'

'You lent him one thousand drachmas?' the Inspector fumed. His cane smashed on to the desk in front of Fletcher. 'You lent a man like Kronos money. A man whom you had never seen before. You are either a bloody liar or a fool!'

'I acted foolishly,' Fletcher mumbled meekly. 'I realise that now. But he had a good boat and he said I could get the money back any time I was in Piraeus.'

'Why did he want the money?'

'He had some clients who wanted to go north to Lemnos and he wanted provisions.'

'So you lent him some money,' the Inspector snarled. He leant forward and poked the leather strips into Fletcher's face.

Fletcher steeled himself. The Inspector was goading him, baiting him to knock the cane out of his hand so he could call in his strongarm boys and beat the answers out of him. But Fletcher was no novice to this kind of treatment.

Eventually the Inspector sat back.

'And that was last year?' he snapped.

'Yes.'

He leant forward again.

'Then why haven't you collected the money before now?'

'I have tried,' Fletcher lied. 'On a number of occasions I have tried, but I have not been able to contact him.'

'You have not seen him since last year?'

'No, Inspector, I assure you. Not since last year.'

The Inspector pierced his eyes.

'If you are lying to me, Fettos,' he snarled, 'I will make it my business to get you. Do you understand?'

Only too well, Fletcher thought.

'Yes, Inspector,' he stammered, 'but I tell you the truth. I have not seen him since last year.'

The Inspector leant back in his chair and

sat silently staring at him. A side door opened and a burly policeman came into the room. The Inspector waved his cane.

'Take him below,' he said, 'and bring the other one in.'

The policeman grabbed Fletcher by the shoulder.

'Inspector, I have done nothing wrong,' Fletcher pleaded.

The Inspector ignored his protest and the policeman bundled him out of the room. Still protesting his innocence, Fletcher allowed himself to be taken down a flight of steps and pushed into a damp, dark cell. Only when the door had been locked behind him, and the policeman had left the cell block, did he stop protesting his innocence and collect his thoughts together.

The Inspector had no grounds for detaining them, he would have to let them go. So long as Mario stuck to their story they would be released in the morning. But the Inspector's reasons for bringing them in still puzzled him. What had he hoped to find out? Why was he so interested in Kronos?

He thought of Zonakas. He could have told the Inspector more about Kronos than Fletcher – or could he? Perhaps Kronos had not been prepared to do business with Zonakas and he had passed the matter over to Greek Security. In which case they were all grasping at straws like Fletcher. He slowly paced the floor of his cell. Whatever the Inspector's reasons, Kronos held the key. It was more important than ever to talk with the man.

An hour later he heard the banging of a cell door in another part of the building and he knew they had finished with Mario. When he wasn't recalled he knew Mario had passed the Inspector's critical examination, and he settled himself down for a night on the hard bunk.

Early the following morning Fletcher was given his belongings and released. Mario was waiting for him in the square outside the police station. Unlike Fletcher, he had not been able to control his temper against the Inspector's baiting and had suffered the consequences. For a few minutes he gave vent to his feelings and cursed the Inspector with every oath he could think of. He also promised various forms of retribution on him. But his night in the station had not been in vain.

'At least I got some news about Kronos,' he grunted.

Fletcher was very interested. 'What?' he asked.

'He is dead!' Mario said.

Fletcher stopped in his tracks. It was his turn to curse. He needed Kronos – alive. It was his only lead.

'Dead! Are you certain?'

'Yes. He was brought into the station last night about nine o'clock.'

'How do you know this, Mario?'

'They put me in a cell with a drunk. He had been fished out of the harbour earlier in the evening and taken to the morgue for treatment. He saw the body.'

Again Fletcher cursed. Without Kronos he was back to square one.

They walked slowly through the back streets towards the north harbour, Mario silently settling his score with the Inspector and Fletcher trying to determine what his next move should be. Their route took them past the church of Saint Peter. When the picturesque old building was in front of them Fletcher looked at the iron studded doors thoughtfully. He had got his last lead from the Patriarch, perhaps he might also get his next one from the same place. He turned to Mario.

'Wait for me, Mario,' he said. 'I think I will go and light a candle for Kronos.'

Mario looked at him with surprise, but knew better than to question his decision. He just shrugged.

Fletcher ran quickly up the steps and entered the church. Despite the early hour he was not the only worshipper. He quickly performed the necessary rituals and sat in the side pew. He didn't have long to wait before the Patriarch joined him.

47

'Kronos is dead,' Fletcher whispered.

The Patriarch mumbled a chant.

'I know, I have been with his widow all night.'

Fletcher paused.

'Did she tell you anything?' he asked.

'She knew nothing, but she heard the name Lofer mentioned.'

Lofer! Fletcher gripped the rail of the pew in front of him. He had also heard the name, from Spencer.

'Who is he?' Fletcher whispered.

'I do not know.'

The Patriarch walked slowly away mumbling his chant.

Fletcher felt a little better. He had a link, a thin link, but nevertheless it tied Spencer's suspicions with Kronos' actions.

When he rejoined Mario he had already made his decision on what to do next. He had to go into Athens and see Spencer.

'Mario,' he said quietly, 'I have to go into Athens on business. I will join you in Nico's bar.'

Mario scratched his head and looked at the church.

'Stefan,' he said thoughtfully. 'How is it your prayers are answered so quickly?'

'I have a special messenger,' Fletcher replied and slapped him on the back.

A half an hour later Fletcher was mingling with the early morning crowd in Athens

Station. He went straight to a public telephone box and dialled Spencer's private number. When Spencer came on the line, Fletcher quickly passed his cryptic message.

'Your laundry is ready,' he said.

'Send it round straight away,' Spencer growled.

'Will you pay cash?'

'Yes.'

'Thank you.'

Fletcher replaced the telephone. From the station he went again by bus to the Acropolis, but this time he had the treasure of antiquity to himself. It was too early for normal sightseers. He selected a seat which gave him an unobstructed view of the road Spencer would use so that he could see if anyone was following him.

When Spencer arrived they got straight down to business.

'If there is something going on it is being kept very quiet,' Fletcher said. 'I drew a blank from all my contacts, except one.' He quickly explained about Kronos, and how he had spent a night in the police station at the invitation of Inspector Ikarios.

'If Ikarios is interested in Kronos,' Spencer growled, 'then he is your man. Ikarios is no fool. He has his ear too close to the ground.'

Fletcher sighed. 'Unfortunately Kronos has been eliminated.'

Spencer was not put off. 'Who was he

working for?'

'I don't know,' Fletcher admitted, 'but his wife heard the name Lofer mentioned.'

'Hm,' Spencer muttered. 'Lofer.'

'Who is he?' Fletcher asked.

'I don't know,' Spencer said regretfully. 'The name was only mentioned to me.'

'By whom?'

Spencer paused. 'Grevosky,' he said.

Fletcher looked at him sharply.

'The Russian attaché?' he asked.

'Yes.'

'That's a turn up for the books,' Fletcher said.

Spencer agreed, but added a word of warning.

'The Russians are foxy devils,' he said. 'You never know what they are up to.'

Fletcher was well aware of this, but nevertheless, it was still surprising that they should be the ones to mention the name.

'What about Zonakas?' Spencer asked.

'He could be involved,' Fletcher said thoughtfully, 'but I rather think he is as much in the dark as we are.'

'What is the next move then?' Spencer asked.

'With Kronos out of the way, our only hope is to find out if this Lofer is fact or fiction.'

'You'll have to be quick,' Spencer warned. 'London have started the ball rolling. They are sending out their vanguard next week. I have to go to Rhodes the day after tomorrow to check security.'

'Don't worry,' Fletcher muttered. 'We'll soon have an answer.'

'How are you going to do it?' Spencer asked.

Fletcher smiled.

'Leave it to me,' he said. 'Have you brought the money?'

'Yes, ten thousand drachmas. Will that be enough?'

'It will have to be,' Fletcher said.

'Don't be too hasty,' Spencer growled. 'We may be barking up the wrong tree.'

Fletcher ignored the remark. With Rassitz on the loose, and Kronos conveniently out of the way, he knew Spencer didn't really mean what he had said.

'Let's get back to Lofer,' Fletcher said, changing the subject. 'Tell me everything that was said.'

But there wasn't much to tell. The name had been mentioned to Spencer in return for a favour. What its significance was remained to be seen.

When Fletcher returned to Piraeus he had already made his plans. In Nico's bar he discussed them with Mario. A Sardinian named Guissepe Mattu had set up an elaborate smuggling ring in Piraeus. He was one of the big time operators and was backed by an international syndicate in Genoa. Mattu had been shot, dead, by the British earlier that week. Fletcher knew of this through Spencer, but not many others were aware of his death. Fletcher intended to become an agent of Mattu's and go openly looking for Lofer in search of business.

'It will be dangerous,' Mario commented.

Fletcher shrugged. It was a risk he was prepared to take. He brought out the money Spencer had given him.

'Let's insure against the danger,' he said. 'See Nico and Toni and get some of their friends to help. I want you to cover me.'

The money exchanged hands. How much went to Mario's contacts didn't interest Fletcher, so long as he kept him alive.

'You'll need a car,' Fletcher added, 'but don't interfere. Keep in the background. See what develops and make sure I stay alive.'

Mario understood what was wanted from him. It wasn't the first time Fletcher had offered himself as a clay pigeon for someone to shoot at. The next few days were going to be very critical.

Later that evening, when the population of Piraeus took their customary stroll in the cool of the day, it was a very different Stefan Fettos who appeared. Gone was his tee shirt and grubby trousers. He was immaculately dressed in an expensive suit. With his tanned face clean shaven and his hair well oiled, he looked like any prosperous Greek business-man. He would be accepted in any society. He had also a respectable address on his calling card. It hadn't taken him long to set himself up. He had rented a three-roomed ground-floor flat in a respectable area of Piraeus away from the harbour. His bed-room overlooked a small park, and the main entrance to the building was on a broad tree-lined avenue. He was ready to look for Lofer!

He started his search in Piraeus itself. First he went to a few well appointed bars, then to a number of third rate hotels, and finally to the second and first class hotels. In each establishment he openly asked the bar attendant, or the desk clerk, if they could put him in touch with Lofer. It took him all the first evening to cover Piraeus. On the second evening he went into Athens and toured the night-clubs and the fleshpots. At the end of the third evening he got the reaction he had anticipated.

It was late when he returned to his apart-ment, but Athens and Piraeus still hummed with life. In the main entrance foyer he hesi-tated. His plastic nameplate on the board which listed the tenants had been turned upside down. It was a warning from Mario! He had company! He braced himself and then relaxed again. This was what he wan-ted. He opened the door of his apartment. The room was dark and quiet. He slipped into the doorway and felt for the electric light switch. Instantly his arm was grabbed and he was pulled into the room! His natural reactions took over and he fought furiously with his assailant. But there was more than one of them and he felt himself being grabbed and pummelled from all sides. His fist connected with someone's face and his foot found a target before he was over-powered. He was forced to the floor, his face pressed into the rough matting carpet and his arms pinned behind his back. There was no talking, the only sound that could be heard was the heavy breathing of the occu-pants. Feverishly he wondered where Mario was. They were playing rougher than he had expected, there was at least three of them. He felt his jacket being pulled off his shoul-ders and his shirt ripped open. A sudden jab in the arm shocked his nerves and des-perately he made a last attempt to get out of their grip, like an animal before the slaughter. He felt the weights on his body being lifted and he sank into unconscious-ness.

When Fletcher came to, his first feeling was the pain in his shoulders. It was as if the muscles were being torn away from his body. His second was a nauseating wave of sickness which twisted at his stomach. He opened his eyes and saw a blurred red vision. He closed them again and allowed his disciplined body to slowly regain its faculties. Gradually his brain began to register. He was on a chair, his arms tied behind his back. The weight of his slumped body was stretching his shoulder muscles. A fresh wave of nausea gripped him. Desperately, he willed himself against vomiting to give himself time to sort out the pieces. He opened his eyes slowly and again saw the red blurred vision. It would be the floor – a red floor. He felt a cool breeze on his face. He was in the open on a red floor! Strong cigar smoke irritated his nostrils and made him retch. His head was suddenly jerked back and a hand started slapping his face until he moved his head to get away from the blows.

'He's conscious,' a man grunted.

Fletcher's brain reacted despite the fog which appeared to engulf it. The man had spoken in German!

The cigar smoke became stronger; it was all around him. Again the man spoke, this time in Greek.

'What do you want with Herr Lofer?'

Fletcher opened his mouth to speak, but the words didn't come out. He opened his eyes and saw a blurred yellow light and then darkness. A vicious slap across his face sent him reeling backwards and he crashed on to a hard floor. His head throbbed violently and he could feel a trickle of blood run down his neck. Vaguely he heard a sharp exchange of words in German and he was lifted back into his seated position.

The man repeated his question, this time less menacingly.

'Business,' Fletcher mumbled. He had to get his faculties together. It was going to be a matter of life or death.

There was a garbled exchange of words directly behind him.

'What sort of business?'

'Guns,' Fletcher said.

'Who told you about Herr Lofer?'

'Kronos,' Fletcher said hoarsely.

There was a long pause. Fletcher lifted his head and opened his eyes. Again there was a blurred yellow light for a few seconds and then darkness. He dropped his head. The blurred red vision began to sort itself out. They were large red tiles. He looked to his right and saw an irregular shaped white object. He tried to focus his eyes.

'You lie!' the man snarled, and pulled Fletcher's head back by the roots of his hair.

'No!' Fletcher cried.

The man released his grip.

'Kronos and I do business,' Fletcher said. 'He told me Lofer might need guns.'

'Well! Why didn't he ask Herr Lofer himself?'

'I do not know,' Fletcher replied hastily, desperately thinking of an answer. 'I have not seen Kronos for three days. I thought he had left Piraeus, so I was asked to contact Lofer.'

'Who asked you?'

'Guissepe Mattu. I work for him.'

'Mattu!'

There was a furtive whispered exchange of German voices. By now Fletcher's brain was functioning as normal. The man who was asking the questions was only relaying orders. Standing behind Fletcher was the man he wanted to see – Herr Lofer!

He allowed his body to slump forward and dropped his head. Slowly he eased his body further forward stretching his shoulder muscles to their limit, so that he could see the ground behind him. He caught a quick glimpse of a pair of brown, calf length boots, before he was roughly dragged up into a seated position again.

'Tell me some of the business deals you have done for Mattu,' the man asked gruffly.

Fletcher had no difficulty in answering. He knew all about Guissepe Mattu – it was his business to know such things.

'A shipment to Saudi Arabia.'

'When?'

'Last month, and last May.'

'Carry on.'

'Small arms shipment to Cyprus, last December.'

He paused as again a whispered conversation was held somewhere behind him. But this time he became conscious of another voice taking part! He listened carefully and caught the high-pitched dulcet tone of a woman's voice!

'Who was your contact in Cyprus?' the man asked.

'Kapilos,' Fletcher mumbled.

Again his head was viciously pulled back. He gritted his teeth as the nerves of his scalp reacted to the harsh treatment. His eyes were closed, but he felt a bright light shining on his face. Footsteps came towards him. Someone was going to have a look at his face! He half opened one of his eyes and saw a blurred white light. The footsteps came right up to him and he caught a fleeting glimpse of a face – a woman's face. And he had seen it before!

The grip on his hair was released and the blood rushed to his head – he felt dizzy. The face – where had he seen it before? It had been familiar.

A sharp voice spoke out clearly in German giving an order. Rough hands grabbed him and his jacket was pulled away from his shoulder. But this time he had no will to resist. He braced himself against the sharp jab of the hypodermic needle and mentally prayed that Mario had his side of the arrangements well under control.

The needle sank into his body and for the second time that night he fell into the deep abyss of unconsciousness.

CHAPTER THREE

Fletcher opened his eyes slowly, and saw the fan swirling the hot, stifling air above him. He was back in his own room, on his bed! His body was surrounded by a pool of perspiration. His head throbbed and he had the same wretched feeling in his stomach that he had had the last time. But he was alive and back in his apartment! He felt much happier.

He heard someone walking around, and he raised himself up on his elbows and caught a glimpse of Mario. He fell back on the bed and allowed his body to gradually sort itself out.

Presently he was able to sit up and take notice. He called out to Mario, who joined him.

'I have some coffee next door,' Mario said.

Fletcher staggered to his feet, and Mario helped him into the adjoining room.

'They play rough, my friend,' Mario muttered. Fletcher didn't answer, but gladly drank the coffee. It helped a little. Afterwards he went into the bathroom and took a shower, that also helped. Gradually he was fit enough to ask a few questions.

'What happened, Mario?'

'There were four of them,' Mario explained. 'One remained in the car and three came into your apartment. They turned up about twenty minutes before you arrived.'

Fletcher grunted. He had guessed there had been three in the room.

'Go on,' he said.

Mario looked crestfallen.

'They bundled you into a car and took the south motorway along the coast towards the peninsula. They gave me the slip soon after they left the motorway.'

'I see,' Fletcher said patiently. 'How did I get here?'

'They brought you back into Piraeus.'

'That was considerate of them.'

'Not really,' Mario said seriously. 'They had intended to dump you in the harbour, but Toni put a spoke in their wheel.'

Fletcher gave a short, low whistle.

'It was as close as that?' he asked quietly.

Mario nodded his head. 'Yes,' he said. 'If Toni hadn't picked up their trail in Glyfada you would have been floating around number seven wharf.'

'I must remember to thank him,' Fletcher muttered, but he didn't dwell on his close proximity to a watery grave. It was one of his occupational hazards. Instead he turned his mind to a more useful form of mental gymnastics – Lofer. He had gone in search of Lofer to see if he existed, now he knew the answer. Not only did Lofer exist, but he was hatching up trouble; everything pointed to it. The Russian's tip off to Spencer had been ominous, Ikarios' presence pointed, but the real danger was the presence of the woman at his interrogation with Lofer. He had only caught a fleeting glimpse of her face, but it had been sufficient. He had seen the face before – on the photograph Spencer had shown him when they had met in the Acropolis. It was Karima Mohmad – a Turk!

'My God, Mario, there's going to be trouble,' he exclaimed suddenly, voicing his thoughts.

Mario wasn't unduly concerned. Trouble was what he lived with in one way and another.

'Is that a change?' he asked.

'No,' Fletcher agreed, 'but this is the kind of trouble we can do without at the moment.' He didn't explain why. The Rhodes conference was a jealously guarded secret, the outcome was absolutely vital to Britain as well as Greece and Turkey. Even Fletcher had been sworn to secrecy.

'They got rid of Kronos in case he talked,' Fletcher explained, 'and they would have done the same with me. The fact that I was supposed to be working for Mattu didn't even concern them, and you know how powerful he was.'

'Perhaps they know he is dead,' Mario said.

'It's unlikely,' Fletcher quickly replied, 'and they didn't give that impression. No, they weren't even interested in Mattu. That means there is something big being organised.'

He started to slowly pace the floor.

'Unless I am mistaken, Mario, Lofer is a German, and one of his guests last night was a Turk.'

Mario made an uncomplimentary remark, but didn't seem surprised.

'Rassitz?' he asked.

'No – a woman, Karima Mohmad. She is a member of the Turkish Embassy.'

This time Mario was surprised.

'I thought all Turkish women were seen, but not heard,' he remarked dryly.

'Not this one Mario, and she is some woman.'

Mario looked at him sharply. It was not like Fletcher to pay such a high compliment.

'I must see this woman,' he said.

'And so you will, Mario, so you will.'

'What do you want me to do? Put a watch on the Turkish Embassy?'

Fletcher thought for a while.

'It will take too long,' he said finally. 'We must look for another lead. Let me have your story again.'

'They arrived here about 2.15. There were four of them.'

'Nationality?'

'Turks.'

'Turks!' Fletcher exclaimed. 'How do you know?'

'They were in a hired car which very conveniently advertised the name of the garage. I checked up this morning. The owner said he thought they were Turks. Any rate, they hired the car last night round about eight o'clock, paid cash, and returned it this morning.'

'Well, it figures,' Fletcher muttered.

'They bundled you into the car and took the east motorway towards the peninsula. I lost them at Glyfada so I went searching for you. Toni remained in the village and I went as far as Voliage. It was like looking for a needle in a haystack, there are so many villas. When I returned to Glyfada, Tony wasn't there, so I came back to Piraeus. He had spotted them on their return and followed them.'

'How long had it taken you to get to Voliage and back?' Fletcher asked thoughtfully.

'About an hour.'

And he had been with Lofer for about half an hour, Fletcher thought, so they couldn't have gone far.

He paced the floor again.

'What is in between Glyfada and Voliage?' he asked.

'The peninsula and Kalafrani Bay. There are a lot of villas round the bay, but the coast is clear.'

'Kalafrani Bay,' Fletcher muttered. Mentally he pictured the geography of the area. The rugged coastline with the peninsula, the small, popular Kalifrani Bay at the head of a deep inlet, the Gaidora Lighthouse. He stopped suddenly.

'The Gaidora Lighthouse!' he exclaimed quietly to himself. 'Of course that was it.'

He turned eagerly to Mario.

'Listen, Mario,' he said excitedly, 'I don't know where I was taken to last night. All I know is that I was out in the open, on a veranda. The ground was paved with red tiles. Occasionally I caught a glimpse of a blurred yellow light. It was like a flashing light.'

'Gaidora Lighthouse?' Mario asked.

'Yes,' Fletcher said firmly. 'It must have been.'

Mario caught his enthusiasm.

'That will narrow the field down,' he said.

'Precisely,' Fletcher agreed. 'Can you see the light from Kalafrani Bay?'

'No,' Mario answered.

'What about further east or north?'

Mario shook his head.

'And west?' Fletcher asked.

'No,' Mario said thoughtfully. 'The only places you can see it are out at sea or on the east side of the peninsula.'

'And that is between Glyfada and Voliage,' Fletcher added.

'There is a narrow track which runs to the point,' Mario explained. 'It joins the road about five kilometres before you reach Voliage.'

Fletcher knew the track. It twisted its way along a steeply wooded and deserted coastline to the point. If he was correct in thinking that the light had come from the lighthouse, then somewhere along that track was the only place he could have seen it.

'Get the car, Mario,' he said. 'We are going to find out if I am right.'

He felt much better now. He had something to hold on to and he wasn't going to let it go. Even if they drew a blank at the peninsula there was always Karima Mohmad. She was no figment of his imagination. He could always play them at their own game. One good turn deserved another. Why should all the strongarm stuff be on their side?

It didn't take them long to reach the track. A fast new motorway covered half the distance and Mario hadn't picked his car at random. They hid the car in some thickets and went along the track on foot. After about ten minutes they saw the sea and the lighthouse. The sea lay beneath them, very calm and very blue, and across the estuary was the lighthouse. It stood, tall and erect, like a proud sentinel guarding the treacherous-looking rocks. Fletcher studied its position closely. Behind it and further to the east the coastline towered over the lighthouse. Its flashing light could not be seen in that direction. Nor would it be seen in Kalafrani Bay or in the village of Voliage, which were at the head of the estuary. If he had seen that light then he had been somewhere along this coastline. He turned his attention to the wooded slopes. Two dwellings nestled in the trees. One was a large, white villa, with a red tiled roof. It stood half-way down the slopes. The other was further along towards the point. It was a modern-looking bungalow in an open clearing. There was nothing else. It had to be one or the other!

Cautiously they followed the track until they came to the villa. In the driveway stood two large, American cars, but there was no other sign of life from the front. Keeping to the woods, they moved into a position where they could observe the rear of the building. Fletcher brought out his binoculars and scanned the well kept lawn and paved veranda, searching for some link with the previous evening. Mario touched his arm and indicated a side door where an elderly couple had appeared. Fletcher watched them walk slowly to the veranda and sit at a table. A few seconds later a maid appeared carrying a tray. He took one last look at the villa and decided to move on.

The bungalow was a further half a kilometre towards the point. It stood in a large clearing and backed on to the sea. As they approached the building they could hear children's voices and a barking dog. Fletcher mentally cursed. It didn't sound very promising. He glanced across at the lighthouse. If he had seen the light then it had to be from this side of the peninsula – and the track terminated at the bungalow! A high wire fence surrounded the grounds and the barking dog prevented them from getting too close. A tradesman's van stood in the open courtyard alongside a small open sports car.

Again they crept into a position where Fletcher could study the rear of the bungalow with his binoculars. Immediately he saw the veranda his pulse quickened. It was paved with large red tiles! And in the centre stood a small white garden statue. He recalled trying to distinguish a vague white object – now he knew what it was.

'This is it,' he whispered excitedly. 'I was on that veranda last night.'

He handed the glasses to Mario. The statue was surrounded by flower boxes and a number of garden seats, but that made no difference. He was convinced that this was where he had been brought to the previous evening.

'What about her?' Mario asked, and handed the glasses back.

A dark, tanned woman in her early thirties had appeared on the veranda with a small child. Fletcher saw the child run across the

67

lawn and disappear over the rocks. A further series of children's cries came from the sea. It hardly seemed the place for an interrogation or a conspiracy, but he was still adamant.

'They could have been in a different part of the building,' he said thoughtfully, 'but this is the place all right.'

'What do we do now?' Mario asked.

'Find out who owns it for a start.'

'And then?'

'Go visiting.'

He saw the tradesman lift a basket out of the van and carry it into the bungalow.

'Mario, go back to the track. When that van appears get a lift from him. He will tell you what we want to know. I will stay here for a while and see what develops. I'll join you back at the car.'

Mario vanished into the trees and Fletcher remained hidden in the bushes, patiently watching the bungalow. The tradesman left soon after Mario, and the only other person to appear was an elderly gardener who poked about in the shrubs and flower beds without making any visible impression. The children's cries continued to carry across from the sea, and occasionally he caught a glimpse of the woman inside the bungalow. The scene appeared completely innocent, except for the tiled veranda, the stone statue, and the unobstructed view of the lighthouse!

Fletcher had gained nothing by staying,

but fortunately Mario had learned a lot from the tradesman.

'The bungalow belongs to a dentist called Pula,' he explained, when Fletcher rejoined him at the car.

'Pula,' Fletcher muttered. 'Does he live here?'

'No, Stefan,' Mario said enthusiastically, 'he doesn't. He lives in Athens. He uses the bungalow as a summer retreat.'

'And the family?' Fletcher asked eagerly.

'They arrived this morning,' Mario explained. 'They are friends of Pula's.'

'So the bungalow was empty last night,' Fletcher said. It was the final confirmation of his suspicions. 'Pula,' he muttered, and rubbed his chin. 'Do you know, Mario, after last night, I think I should have my teeth seen to.'

'Is it wise to visit him?' Mario asked. 'If he was with Lofer last night, he will recognise you.'

Fletcher paused before replying. The advantages were all on Pula's side. The only alternative was to put a watch on the man and hope he led them to someone else. But that was a slow, time-taking business, and it wasn't certain to get results. It was also possible that Pula was completely innocent. His bungalow could have been used without him knowing. On the other hand, if Pula was involved and Fletcher exposed himself it would at lest bring some sort of reaction, dangerous or otherwise.

'He may be innocent,' Fletcher said. 'In which case we will be wasting a lot of time waiting for him to make a move. If he is in league with Lofer, it is unlikely that he will attempt any reprisals on me from his surgery. No, I think I will go and see him.'

He glanced at his watch. The afternoon siesta period was over. Pula would be back at work.

It wasn't difficult to locate Pula's residence, or his surgery. They were one and the same. A telephone directory provided the information. They were on the top floor of a modern, five-storey building, in a fashionable district in the west of Athens.

Mario drove slowly past the building.

'Do you want me to come with you?' he said.

'No, stay in the car. Drive around the block and drop me at the end of the road. It will be better that I am not seen leaving the car.'

Mario quickly toured the block and deposited Fletcher out of sight of the building. By the time Fletcher had walked up to the entrance to the apartments, Mario was already parked on the opposite side of the road, in the shade of a large, overhanging tree.

Pula's surgery adjoined his apartment. His

name was printed across the glass entrance door to his reception room. Fletcher straightened his tie and without knocking entered the room. Sitting at a desk was a young, slim girl, in a neat, white starched, overall. There was no one else in the room. The girl looked up, surprised, when he entered the room.

'Good afternoon,' Fletcher said, 'I wonder if I could see Mr Pula?'

She looked slightly confused.

'Mr Pula has a patient and he does not see anyone unless they have an appointment.'

Fletcher walked over to her, leant on her desk and looked her full in the face.

'I have no appointment,' he said firmly, 'but I would like Mr Pula to have a look at my teeth, and perhaps we can arrange a number of visits.'

She could tell him he was determined and hurriedly opened the appointment book which lay in front of her.

'There is another patient due in fifteen minutes,' she said apologetically.

'Tell Mr Pula I have been specially recommended to him.'

He contemplated mentioning Lofer's name, but decided to use it as a last resort.

The receptionist hesitated and then capitulated.

'What name is it please?'

'Fettos.'

She stood up and, backing away from him,

entered the surgery. Instantly Fletcher had the appointment book open and was scanning the pages. Mentally he repeated the patients' names. Suddenly one of them sounded familiar – Dr Sleitser! With mounting curiosity he repeated the name. Dr Sleitser! Was this significant? he wondered. His brain raced over the facts he knew about the Doctor. He had seen him with the Professor at the Acropolis the day he had gone to meet Spencer. He was an archaeologist working on one of the islands. He was German! Fletcher clenched his fist. My God, he thought, it could be very significant!

He quickly closed the book when he heard the receptionist return.

'If you will take a seat, Mr Pula will see you in a few minutes. He is nearly finished with his present patient.'

Fletcher thanked her and sat down, his mind still preoccupied with the fact that Dr Sleitser was one of Pula's patients.

A few minutes later the surgery door opened and Pula appeared with his patient. He was tall for a Greek, but still smaller than Fletcher. He had a serious-looking face and a prominent nose on which rested a pair of thick-rimmed spectacles. After dispensing with his patient, he came over to Fletcher. There was no visible sign of recognition, but this meant nothing to Fletcher. He could have been prepared for the meeting when the receptionist gave him Fletcher's name.

'Come in,' he said politely.

Fletcher followed him into the surgery.

'Sit in the chair,' Pula said. 'I am afraid I can only look at your teeth today. I have another patient coming.' He walked over to a desk and Fletcher took his place in the dentist's chair.

'I understand,' Fletcher said, watching him closely.

Pula started to make some notes on a small pad.

'The receptionist said you were recommended to me,' he remarked.

'Yes,' Fletcher replied slowly.

Pula had his back to him and was still writing his notes.

'Who by, Mr Fettos?'

Fletcher hesitated. It wasn't the ideal moment, but he couldn't afford to let the opportunity pass.

'Herr Lofer,' he said. He couldn't see Pula's face, but he noticed he had momentarily stopped writing! There was a short delicate silence. Pula had been caught off guard!

'Herr Lofer?' Pula asked. 'I don't know a Herr Lofer.'

'He gave me your name,' Fletcher persisted.

Pula finished his writing and walked over to his instrument tray.

'There are a lot of dentists in this area,' he said calmly, 'and my name is not uncommon.'

There was only one Pula in the district, Fletcher thought, and he knows it.

'Do you own a bungalow on the point near Voliage?'

'Why do you ask?'

'Herr Lofer told me you did.'

The dentist played with his instruments.

'Well, I do not know him,' he said, but he didn't answer Fletcher's question. 'It is of no consequence,' he added.

He started to examine Fletcher's mouth, but it was not with the expert touch Fletcher had anticipated. The dentist had been knocked off balance!

'There is a filling missing,' Pula said. 'I will attend to it, but you will have to come back for further treatment.'

Fletcher became suspicious. A few minutes earlier, Pula had not been prepared to give him more than a cursory examination. Now he was offering to do much more!

'I see you have had a blow to your head,' Pula remarked. He had walked behind the chair on which Fletcher was sitting, to a small wall cupboard.

'Yes, I got into a spot of trouble last night,' Fletcher replied. He leant forward and quickly adjusted a small table mirror so that he could see what Pula was up to.

'Do you live in Athens?' Pula asked.

Fletcher watched him silently unlock the cupboard and take out a small glass phial.

'In Piraeus,' Fletcher replied casually.

He couldn't see what Pula was doing now, but he had a shrewd idea. He was preparing a hypodermic injection! Fletcher recalled the previous evening when he had been drugged by an injection from a similar instrument. Was Pula planning to do the same?

The dentist returned to face him.

'Keep this spring in your mouth,' he said, and leant forward and inserted the instrument in Fletcher's mouth. Fletcher braced himself. When he saw the hypodermic needle suddenly appear he grabbed Pula's arm to stop him. He saw the dentist's cheek muscles go taut, and Pula tried to force the needle towards his face. For a fleeting moment the two men were locked in a trial of strength. Suddenly Pula gave way and allowed his arm to be pushed to one side.

'This is only to kill the pain,' Pula fumed, his face flushed with anger.

Fletcher removed the spring from his mouth.

'No injection,' he said firmly. 'I can stand the pain.'

The dentist clashed the hypodermic on to the glass-topped table.

'As you wish,' he snapped.

Fletcher replaced the spring in his mouth

and Pula proceeded to attend to the tooth. But the atmosphere was strained. The dentist quickly did what was necessary with even less polish than he had displayed earlier. His attitude, however, had confirmed Fletcher's suspicions. Pula was linked with Lofer! But how? And why? He hadn't been at the bungalow the previous evening, Fletcher felt certain, so where did he fit into the plot? Was he acting as the link man, providing Lofer with accommodation? And what about Dr Sleitser? Was his name in the appointment book a coincidence, or something more pertinent?

'Come back tomorrow, at the same time,' Pula said abruptly. He opened the door to his reception room. 'Good day.'

Fletcher thanked him and left the surgery. In the corridor outside the reception room, however, he paused for a moment and then reopened the reception door. Pula was standing by the receptionist's desk, the telephone in his hand. When he saw Fletcher his face clouded over and he replaced the telephone on its stand. His hasty action told Fletcher all he wanted to know. Fletcher had put his head in the hornet's nest and stirred up trouble. Pula was quickly passing on the news – too quickly.

'Well?' Pula asked.

'What time did you say tomorrow?' Fletcher asked calmly.

'Five o'clock,' Pula said irritably.

Fletcher thanked him and closed the door. He had set the ball rolling. If only he knew where it rolled to, he would be a lot closer to solving the mystery. Who was Pula in such a hurry to contact on the telephone?

At the entrance to the building, Fletcher hesitated. He saw Mario sitting in the car, and made a quick decision to return to Piraeus by train. He crossed the road and walked towards a bus stop. This took him past the car. Fortunately Mario had the window open and was leaning against the door. As he came alongside the car, Fletcher talked to the air in front of him. 'I will see you back at the flat,' he said. 'You stay here and see if Pula has any sudden visitors.'

Mario made no reply – Fletcher didn't expect him to. In full view from the dentist's window, Fletcher boarded a bus which took him to the station in the centre of the city. But he had just missed the train to Piraeus. Rather than hang around the crowded railway station, he strolled into the nearby market and purchased some provisions. When he returned to the station, there was a train standing at the platform No sooner had he taken his seat, however, than he realised he was being followed. A sixth sense, almost like a built-in radar system, gave him the alert. He had noticed, in the market, the small slim man in the crumpled fawn suit, who had just entered the compartment. He had also seen him before that, standing on the railway platform. It was more than a coincidence. He relaxed and looked out of the window. If he was being followed, he didn't want to give the man any indication that he was aware of his presence. Not until he knew who he worked for!

The train quickly covered the short distance from Athens into Piraeus, but Fletcher purposely waited until they reached the harbour before alighting. It was an area he knew well. It was an area where he had friends. The man in the crumpled suit also left the train at the same station!

From the station, Fletcher slowly skirted the harbour and gradually made his way towards Nico's bar. Like a person used to such a situation, he gave the man behind him every opportunity to keep a respectable distance without losing his prey. Only on the last leg did Fletcher purposely lose his man. Quickly he darted through the narrow lanes and into the small, dark, bar. Nico was in his customary pose, glass and cloth in hand. A handful of locals sat in a corner under a blue haze, quietly drinking ouzo. No one looked up when he entered, only Nico nodded his head in recognition. Fletcher went up to him.

'There is a man tailing me,' he whispered. 'Small, wearing a fawn suit and trilby. I want to know who he works for.'

Nico nodded his head knowingly. Fletcher put a ten drachma note on the counter, not for Nico, but for one of his boys. Nico indicated his stock room, and Fletcher left him to make his own arrangements. For about a quarter of an hour Fletcher sat in the small back room silently studying the various labels on the bottles and contemplating the graceful lines of the wine casks.

When Nico joined him, he still had the glass and cloth in his hand. For a moment he stood grim faced. Then he dispensed with the cigarette from his mouth and said: 'He's gone.'

Fletcher stood up.

'Thanks, Nico. Who was he?'

Nico paused.

'One of Veti's men.'

Fletcher looked at him. Their eyes met.

'Sure?' he asked, but didn't doubt the answer.

Nico nodded his head. 'Sure,' he muttered.

Fletcher swore; he had enough on his plate without having to contend with the Communists. Why had they entered the field? Spencer had told him that the Russians had tipped him off about Lofer, so why should they now be interested?

He had never met Veti, but he knew of him, well enough. He was a Greek and a Communist. In many ways he was their counterpart to Fletcher. Only he had been trained by the K.G.B. and worked strictly to orders – usually from the Kremlin, or Prague, or Budapest, depending upon who was making the play.

'Watch your step,' Nico said quietly. 'Don't let them get too close.'

'I don't intend to,' Fletcher said grimly.

He left the bar to return to his apartment. He wasn't feeling quite so elated as he had been earlier. The nature of his work had suddenly changed. He was in the big league now. With the Communists hovering about it became an East versus West issue. But their presence puzzled him more than annoyed him. Up till now there had not been the slightest whisper of their interest, and he had put out a wide enough net to pick up any of their moves. Why the sudden flexing of their muscles? he wondered. Were they just watching from the sidelines? It wasn't unusual Even if they were not involved they didn't like to be uninformed. They could be only on the fringe looking for any scraps to pick up. But on the other hand, he knew they could be deeply involved. In which case the sooner he got to the bottom of it the better. Their interest could only spell danger for Britain. It would certainly suit the Communists' motives to wreck the Rhodes Conference.

CHAPTER FOUR

'Good afternoon!'

The man sitting in the chair smiled blandly. His hands rested on his knee under his trilby hat. He was a Turk, there was no question about it, and he spoke in a rough, broken accent.

Fletcher closed the door and entered the apartment. He didn't like uninvited visitors, even polite ones. He noticed the Turk's bruised cheek bone and wondered if they had met before. He ignored the welcome and crossed over to the veranda. There was only one car parked outside – Mario's.

'I am alone,' the Turk said. His Greek was only just understandable.

'You can speak in your own tongue,' Fletcher snapped. 'Then there will be no misunderstanding.'

Again the Turk smiled.

'As you wish,' he said in Turkish.

'What do you want?' Fletcher asked.

'Not trouble,' the Turk said. 'This is purely a social call.'

'Well, I am afraid I can't offer you a drink,' Fletcher said sarcastically.

The Turk shrugged.

'There may be other occasions,' he smiled.

'Le's stop beating about the bush,' Fletcher said. 'What are you after?'

The Turk didn't answer, he was staring at the entrance door, his face hard set.

'It is my partner,' Fletcher explained.

Mario entered the apartment. Immediately he saw the Turk his hand went for his knife. In a flash the Turk had removed the trilby from his knee and was brandishing a small, but lethal, automatic. It was pointing at Mario.

'Tell him I don't want any trouble,' he said to Fletcher.

'It's a social call,' Fletcher said dryly.

Mario scowled. 'He is one of the four who called last night,' he snarled.

'I rather gathered that,' Fletcher said, and purposely walked over to the opposite side of the room from Mario, so presenting the Turk with a divided target.

'Well?' he asked.

'My employer would like to meet you,' the Turk said.

'What about?'

'Business.'

'What sort of business?'

'Your kind.'

They were going around in circles.

'Who is your employer?' Fletcher asked.

The Turk smiled.

'Let us call her my employer.'

Fletcher looked at him sharply.

'Her?' he asked.

'Yes – her.'

Fletcher looked at the bruise on his face and the gun in his hand. He had a good idea who his employer was. It was a surprising turn up for the books, but he had wanted to meet Karima Mohmad again. It appeared that he was getting his opportunity sooner than he had expected.

'I thought your women looked after the children and did the cooking,' Mario sneered, trying to bait the Turk.

'There are exceptions,' the Turk said evenly.

'Who is this woman?' Fletcher asked.

'Why don't you come and find out?'

'When?'

'This evening.'

Fletcher glanced at Mario. He was leaning against the wall, his eyes watching the Turk.

'How much money is there in it for us?' Mario asked.

'More than you will earn by sitting on your backsides on your boat,' the Turk replied.

They had been checking on them, Fletcher thought. They meant business. It sounded promising.

'In that case,' he said, 'we will do as you say.'

The Turk put his revolver in a holster under his left armpit and stood up.

'Be at the junction of Leaferos and Rangavi at nine o'clock this evening. A white car will be parked there. I will be in it. Follow me and I will take you to the house of my employer.'

He raised his hat and smiled at them.

'Until this evening,' he said and left the room.

Mario went to the veranda window.

'I don't like it, Stefan,' he said. 'It could be a trap. They tried to kill you last night, but failed. We could be putting our heads into the lion's den.'

Fletcher was well aware of this.

'But why go to all the bother of getting us into Athens? All they need do is sit in the first bar along the front and when it is dark – woosh!'

'We have too many friends in Piraeus and there are too many eyes. In Athens there will be only them and us.'

'In that case we will take precautions,' Fletcher said. 'I will go alone – or rather I will appear to go alone, but you can be around in case of trouble.'

Mario agreed; anything was preferable to going blindly to a meeting with the Turks.

'There's more trouble brewing,' Fletcher warned. 'I was followed from the station by one of Veti's men.'

Mario swore.

'I wonder who tipped them off,' he said.

'They may be involved,' Fletcher said.

'In Cyprus?' Mario asked.

'Not necessarily in Cyprus, but in trouble. There are certain diplomatic moves afoot, Mario, which will require time and patience to bring them to fruition. If the Communists start stirring it up it could upset the apple-cart.'

'We could always find out,' Mario suggested.

'How?' Fletcher asked.

Mario withdrew his dagger and playfully fingered it.

'We know where Veti lives and we know his contacts. Why not bring one of his boys in for questioning?'

Mario liked to mix it. To him you either worked with someone or against them. If he was an enemy you fought him and if necessary killed him. War was war, not a game of chess. But for the professional spy there were certain unwritten rules. You didn't kill your opposite number unless it was the last resort, because you knew that someone else would take his place. There would be no vacuum. And the someone who filled the vacuum might well kill you. Instead of killing them, you either dealt with them, watched them, used them, or made sure that at the final play the ball landed in the right court.

'No, Mario,' he said. 'At the moment they aren't doing any harm. We'll let them keep their distance. If they get too close, then we'll act.'

'Not even a little warning?' Mario asked hopefully.

'No,' Fletcher said firmly. 'Not even that.'

Mario shrugged and put his dagger away.

'Did Pula have many visitors?' Fletcher asked.

'Yes,' Mario said. 'Ikarios!'

'Ikiarios!' Fletcher exclaimed. It was proving to be a very eventful day. 'I wonder if that was the result of my visit or whether Ikarios is chasing the same thing we are? Did he see you?'

'No, Stefan. He didn't seem concerned about any of the cars parked about.'

'Why should he be?' Fletcher asked. There was something in Mario's tone which had raised his suspicions.

'Because there was also a cream Mercedes watching the apartment!'

'How do you know?'

'Because it is now further along the boulevard waiting for us to make a move! It has just arrived.'

Fletcher quickly crossed to the veranda and saw the car about a hundred metres away.

'Same registration number?' he asked.

'Same one,' Mario muttered.

'When did it turn up outside Pula's apartment block?'

'It was there when we arrived. It left soon after you but came back. It was still there when I left.'

'It left soon after me,' Fletcher said thoughtfully. 'Did you notice anything different when it returned? About the occupants, I mean, was there one less for instance?'

Mario shook his head.

'I hadn't given it much attention until it returned,' he said regretfully. 'There were certainly two of them in the car then.'

'I think that's what put Veti on to me,' Fletcher said. 'They must have recognised me when I came out of the building. They assumed I was returning to Piraeus by train, so they dropped one of their men off at the station to wait for me. Then they returned to keep watch on Pula.'

'Why should they be watching Pula?' Mario asked.

'Or us?' Fletcher added. 'I can only guess they are as much in the dark as we are.'

'And Inspector Ikarios the same?'

'I'm not sure about him,' Fletcher said truthfully. 'He's a bit of an outsider.'

He looked out of the veranda again. The Mercedes was still there. Veti was now part of the act.

'We'll have to get rid of them tonight,' he said pensively, 'before we meet our friend.'

He turned away from the veranda. The men in the Mercedes were going to have a

87

long, fruitless vigil.

At 8.30 that evening Fletcher and Mario drove into Athens. The Mercedes followed a short distance behind. Fletcher waited until they were in the heart of the capital before giving them the slip – it wasn't difficult. From the city centre he then drove to the road junction the Turk had given him. The white car was standing waiting for him and pulled away as soon as Fletcher drove up behind him. Together they drove out of the city and into the summer retreat of Athens, a suburb of lush gardens and expensive villas.

The Turk pulled up outside a large iron gate which guarded the entrance to a residence hidden behind the trees and shrubs. But on the gate was its name – Villa Acancia. Fletcher knew of it – it belonged to the Turkish Embassy! He parked his car behind the Turk.

'Where is your partner?' the Turk asked.

'He has other business to attend to,' Fletcher lied.

The Turk looked at him suspiciously, but let the matter pass.

'We'll walk from here,' he said.

Fletcher hesitated. Once behind the iron gates he was on Turkish territory. They could deal with him as they wished, without interference. It wasn't an encouraging thought.

'Hurry,' the Turk urged.

Fletcher shrugged off his fears and followed him, thankful that Mario was not far away.

They walked a short distance along the drive and then took a side track through the bushes and came to an annexe to the main building. In the brightly lit entrance hallway sat another tough-looking Turk. His jacket was open, displaying the same equipment the other Turk had exhibited in Fletcher's apartment. It must be standard issue, Fletcher thought. The Turk got off his seat and opened the glass door for them.

Fletcher was told to wait in the hallway whilst his escort entered a side room. A few seconds later he reappeared and motioned Fletcher to join him in the room. It was a large room, brightly lit, with a scented atmosphere. Across the floor lay a number of Persian rugs. At one end was a small cocktail bar and immediately opposite the entrance door was an open balcony.

There were only two other occupants in the room in addition to Fletcher and his escort, Karima Mohmad and her brother Kasim!

For several seconds nothing was said as all parties openly appraised each other. Fletcher liked what he saw. She was even more attractive than her photographs had shown. She possessed all the natural beauty typical of her

89

race – long, dark brown hair, dark exciting eyes, sparkling, even, white teeth, and a full well-proportioned figure. But her window dressing and bearing had all the hallmarks of a strong western influence. Her jewellery glistened and her gold cocktail dress gripped her body and accentuated the right curves. To Fletcher she was one of the most exciting women he had met for along time. Reluctantly, he turned his attention to her brother who was wearing a white dinner jacket. He was the same height as his sister and in many ways bore the same resemblance. He frowned when he saw Fletcher looking at him and looked away.

'Good evening, Mr Fettos,' the woman said. Her voice was soft, her Greek accent flawless.

'Good evening,' Fletcher smiled. 'I am afraid you have an advantage over me. I was not told your name.'

'My name is of no consequence,' she said, 'but, if you wish to address me, call me Salunda.'

'Salunda!' Fletcher repeated the name. 'Nice.' He nodded his head approvingly. 'It suits you.'

'I have not asked you here to discuss my name,' she snapped. Her brother stood beside her scowling.

Fletcher smiled confidently. 'I didn't think you had … Salunda.'

Kasim looked even more irritated.

'What will you have to drink, Mr Fettos?'

'Nothing,' Fletcher said. He sat on one of the stools and carefully lit a cigarette.

She gave him a questioning look.

'It might be drugged,' he explained.

He saw her flush up, so did Kasim.

'Why should I do that to you?' she snapped.

'Why did you do it last night?' he asked evenly.

There was an electric silence, the atmosphere became tense. The Turk who had brought him went for his automatic.

'No, Ahmad,' Salunda said hurriedly.

Fletcher was watching him closely.

'How did you know?' she asked calmly.

'I recognised the ankles,' Fletcher lied.

Kasim turned his back on Fletcher and spoke to his sister.

'Do we have to deal with this insolent cut-throat?' he asked. He had spoken in Turkish but it had the soft rolling accent typical of the Cypriot Turks. Fletcher didn't give any indication that he spoke their language, although Ahmad was aware of it.

'Yes, Kasim, we have to,' Salunda said quietly. 'You know he has agreed to our plan. We must stick to it.' She turned her attention back to Fletcher.

'For you information, Mr Fettos,' she said, 'if it had not been for me, you would not

91

have survived last night.'

It was Fletcher's turn to look surprised.

'There was no need to take you back to Piraeus, we could have killed you any time, but if you really were an agent of Mattu's, I assumed you would have friends looking out for you. I was correct. Your friend followed Ahmad from Glyfada. We allowed him to stop us from disposing of your body.'

Fletcher looked hard at her. She was deadly earnest.

'Why?' he asked.

'Because I want some information from you and a business deal.'

Fletcher was both curious and interested, but it didn't pay to appear too eager.

'I'm interested if it pays well,' he said.

'It will.'

She lit a cigarette.

'Where is Kronos?' she asked sharply.

The question took Fletcher by surprise. What was her interest in Kronos?

'I haven't seen him for three days,' he replied. 'You heard me last night.'

'You said a number of things last night which weren't true. That is why my men didn't kill you. Now I want the truth.'

Fletcher hesitated. She was in league with Lofer. Furthermore she was a Turkish Cypriot and probably one of the ringleaders of whatever plot was being hatched. To her, Fletcher was a gun-runner, smuggler and agent of Mattu. If she continued to think this and he could be of use to her, then she might well take him into her employ. At any rate it was worth a try. He had nothing to lose by telling the truth.

'Kronos is dead,' he said.

The remark brought an urgent whispered remark from Kasim, but his sister quickly silenced him.

'When?' she asked.

'Two days ago.'

'How?'

Fletcher shrugged. 'I don't know. His wife was called into the police station to identify the body.'

'Police!' Kasim exclaimed.

'Who told you about Lofer?' Salunda asked, ignoring her brother.

'Kronos,' Fletcher replied. 'We used to work together before I joined Mattu. He had some private deal with Lofer. When I heard he was dead I thought I might get the order.'

'You still work for Mattu?'

Fletcher hesitated momentarily, and made a quick decision.

'No,' he said. 'Mattu was shot, dead, seven days ago running guns into Saudi Arabia, but I know his contacts in Genoa. I could still arrange a shipment.'

'He lies,' Kasim snapped.

'No,' Salunda said. 'He is telling the truth. Mattu was shot by the British last week.

They have kept it quiet; not many people know.'

Fletcher congratulated himself. She had been testing him. But she had kept quiet when he had lied the previous evening. Why? What was her game? Was she wanting to arrange her own shipment? Was that why she had spared his life? Or was there some other deeper reason?

'You have a boat?' she asked.

'Yes.'

'I would like to hire it for two days with you and your crew.'

'How much?'

'One thousand drachmas a day.'

'Two thousand,' Fletcher said. 'Times are hard.'

Kasim became irritated with the bargaining. Again he turned to Salunda and spoke to her in Turkish.

'Do it my way,' he pleaded.

'No, Kasim. It is as we agreed.'

His face clouded over. He didn't like her decision.

'Fifteen hundred drachmas,' she said.

'Agreed,' Fletcher replied. 'What do you want me to do?'

She opened a drawer and brought out a map which she unfolded and spread over a small table. Fletcher joined her and took in her strong scented perfume.

She put her finger on a small bay about

four kilometres east of Athena, but before she said anything there was a knock at the door. She hesitated as Ahmad attended to it. Fletcher watched their faces. Ahmad looked at Salunda and nodded his head.

'Show him in the other room,' she said. 'I won't be long.'

Another visitor, Fletcher thought. Another business proposition, or was it social?

'There is a small sand beach here,' she explained. 'Be there at 12.30. Do not leave Piraeus before midnight, and use no lights.'

Fletcher took a last look at the map.

'How far will we be going?' he asked. 'There is the question of fuel.'

'It will take about seven to eight hours.'

That gave him a radius of about ninety to one hundred kilometres, he thought.

'Anything else?' she asked.

'Who will meet me at the bay?'

She indicated the Turk who had escorted him to the bungalow.

'Ahmad will be there.'

'What is the purpose of our journey?' he asked probing.

'Does it matter to you?' she asked.

Fletcher shrugged.

'It depends,' he said. 'I value my life.'

'Your life will not be in danger,' she said impatiently. 'Now I have other business to attend to. Ahmad will show you out.'

She turned her back on him. Their meeting

was at an end. Fletcher cast one last appreciative glance at her seductive curves, and walked towards the door. In the hallway she hesitated. The Turk who had been sitting there had opened a door to the room opposite. Fletcher cast a quick glance in the room, saw the man waiting to join Salunda, and hurriedly left. It was Pula! He was wearing evening dress. If he hadn't come across the dentist sooner, he would have deduced it was purely a social call, but now he knew different. The dentist was mixing business with pleasure!

The Turk escorted Fletcher back to the car, but he was allowed to return to Athens by himself. He drove a short way along the route, and then returned and picked up Mario.

'Well?' he asked.

Mario gave a broad grin. 'She is some woman, Stefan.'

'No fool, neither,' Fletcher added.

Mario sighed. 'There are always drawbacks. No woman is perfect.'

'What did you see?'

'A maid, a cook, and two strongarm men. All Turks.'

'And the residence?'

'There was a man patrolling the grounds, so I left it alone.'

'You heard the proposition?'

'Yes. An eight hour trip and back again.'

'Where will that take us?'

'To one of the islands, or perhaps to Kavouri along the coast.'

'Or well out to sea,' Fletcher added thoughtfully.

Mario looked at him questioningly.

'What are you thinking of, my friend?'

'Rassitz,' Fletcher said. 'It is about time he turned up.'

'We are a long way from Cyprus,' Mario said.

Fletcher sighed.

'I was hoping to stop him from getting there,' he muttered, and changed the subject. 'Did you see their visitor arrive?'

'Yes, he came by car. Tall, slim, elderly with glasses. He was wearing a dinner jacket.'

'That was Pula,' Fletcher said.

'Ah!' Mario beamed. 'The plot thickens. A Greek and a Turk doing business. A strange combination.'

Fletcher agreed. It was a strange combination, but he wasn't thinking of Pula and Salunda alone. There were Lofer and Veti to contend with also. Lofer had shown his iron fist and Veti had the might of the K.G.B. behind him. It wasn't going to be a picnic. But despite the danger signals, Fletcher was at least beginning to feel he was getting somewhere. It had been a good move to set himself up as Mattu's agent. Not only had it confirmed Lofer's existence, it had also brought him into Salunda's service. Their trip that evening sounded promising. Besides the clandestine arrangements, the very fact that she had hired him and not one of the more respectable firms suggested that it had an illicit purpose!

When they reached Piraeus they gave their apartment a wide berth in case Veti's men were still looking for them. They hid the car in a courtyard behind Nico's bar and went to the *Tonos* by foot.

A few minutes before midnight they weighed anchor and nosed the *Tonos* silently out of the crowded harbour into the open sea. It was a dark night but the sea was calm. Shortly before the appointed time they arrived at the bay Salunda had indicated, and ran the boat on to the fine sand. Fletcher jumped ashore and waited. It was a quiet secluded bay, and the road from Athens was only a short distance away. At twelve-thirty, precisely, two dark figures appeared as if from nowhere. One of them was Ahmad.

'I have a passenger for you,' he said.

'Tell him to get aboard,' Fletcher said.

The man with Ahmad did as Fletcher had said, and Fletcher pushed the boat off the sand bed before joining him.

'Take him below,' he said to Mario and went to the wheel-house. He started the engine, and nosed the boat out of the bay.

Presently, Mario joined him. He seemed highly amused.

'Our passenger wants to see you,' he said and gave a knowing wink.

Fletcher handed the wheel over to him and went below.

'Good evening, again, Mr Fettos.'

Fletcher stopped in his tracks at the entrance to the saloon. It was Salunda!

'Good evening,' he grunted, and gave a deep, nervous cough, which he was prone to when caught off guard. She smiled at him – a mocking smile, as if she was enjoying his embarrassment. He entered the saloon and sat on one of the bunks. He could be excused for having mistaken her for a man, earlier. She was wearing a navy blue shirt and slacks, and a silk scarf was wrapped around her head. But despite her attire there was nothing masculine about her. He gave another cough as he realised he was staring at her, and looked quickly around the saloon. It was hardly the place to entertain a woman. The remains of the supper lay scattered across the table and various objects of clothing lay on the bunks. The bulkhead surrounding Mario's bunk was adorned with a fine selection of pin-ups, all depicting the female form in various stages of undress.

'You are surprised to see me?' she asked teasingly.

'This is not quite the ideal place for a

woman,' he said, and again coughed.

She raised her eyebrows questioningly.

'Why not?' she asked.

'This is not a luxury yacht,' he said.

'No,' she mused, 'but then your lady friends over your bunk haven't objected. That is your bunk?' She was playing with him like a female kitten. Fletcher decided to play her at her own game.

'But they aren't flesh and blood like you,' he said. 'My partner and I have often wished they were. We have definite views on how we would entertain them, and in our business you have to take your opportunities when you can get them.'

He gave her a broad wink and ran his eyes approvingly over her figure.

She flushed up. 'You wouldn't dare,' she snapped, her playful attitude gone.

'Why not?' Fletcher shrugged. 'We are not gentlemen. We are gun-runners, smugglers. Who knows what tomorrow will bring?'

'But you are also Greeks,' she retorted, 'and you Greeks prefer money to sex. You haven't been paid yet. Lay a finger on me and you won't receive one drachma.'

'True,' Fletcher replied thoughtfully. 'Money means a lot to us, but,' he added secretively, 'I would rate you higher than three thousand drachmas!'

'I've had enough of this talk,' she fumed, and opened her handbag and produced a small calibre pistol. 'I won't hesitate to use this if necessary,' she warned.

Fletcher again coughed and slapped his knee.

'Well, now that we understand each other,' he said, 'which bunk would you prefer?'

'I will decide later,' she said coldly, 'but you and your partner will be sleeping on deck.' She quickly changed the subject before Fletcher could retaliate with any alternative suggestion.

'I want to discuss business,' she said. 'Have you got a chart?'

Fletcher produced a chart of the area from one of the drawers. She indicated the island of Serifos.

'That is where I want to go,' she said.

'Serifos.' Fletcher repeated the name. It had been a long time since he had been there. He looked at the chart. It wasn't a big island and there were only two harbours, one in the town of Serifos and the other at the north end of the island.

'It will take us about seven hours,' he said.

'I want you to anchor off the south coast of Kithnos tonight. I don't want to arrive at Serifos before nine o'clock in the morning.'

'As you wish,' Fletcher muttered and wondered why.

'There is a small bay about twelve kilometres north of Serifos. I want you to land me at nine o'clock. You are then to go into

Serifos, but return and pick me up at midday.'

'What do we do in Serifos?' Fletcher asked.

'Look around,' Salunda said.

'For what?'

'Nothing in particular. You are an observant man, Fettos. If you see anything of interest you can let me know.' Again she had the teasing, playful expression on her face. What was she up to? Fletcher wondered. What was he expected to see? Or was it just a blind whilst she attended to her business?

'And what will you be doing?' he asked.

She looked at him with surprise.

'That is no concern of yours,' she snapped. 'You are paid to do as you are told.'

'I am not interested in your business,' Fletcher replied evenly, 'but I have been in the game too long not to take precautions. Even the simplest of plans can often go wrong. All I want to know is where to contact you if it should become necessary.'

She didn't reply straight away.

'Do you know the Order of Barnabas?' she asked.

'Yes,' Fletcher said, surprised. 'They have a monastery on Cyprus.'

'They also have a retreat on Serifos. My uncle is a member of the order. That is where I am going. It is close to the bay where you will land me. Does that satisfy you?'

Fletcher coughed. 'I thought all Turks

102

were Moslems,' he said.

'My uncle is not of my race or my faith,' she snapped straight back at him.

'I see,' Fletcher muttered, but he would have liked to question her further. He didn't doubt that the retreat existed, or of its connection with the Order of Barnabas, but he doubted the purpose of her visit.

'Now, if you will collect what you need, you can leave,' she said haughtily.

Fletcher slowly brought himself to his full height. Her tone had a master–servant ring about it which he didn't like. She was standing waiting for him to leave like a princess dismissing her courtier. She had had her play with him and attended to her business, now he was to leave. He felt a sudden urge to lift her up and shake her off her pedestal, but he restrained himself. So long as she employed him he was close to the kernel and that was where he wanted to be. He couldn't afford to upset her.

Slowly he gathered a few essentials together, and went to the doorway. As a last defiant gesture, he turned and looked at her.

'I hope you have pleasant dreams, Salunda,' he said in his deep, resonant voice, 'because I will.'

As he climbed the short flight of steps on to the deck, he heard the door being closed behind him, and the bolts being rammed noisily into position.

Mario gave a chuckle of delight from the wheelhouse.

'She likes you, Stefan,' he beamed. 'I can tell.'

Fletcher gave an embarrassed grunt.

'Set a course for Kithnos,' he said. 'We will anchor off the south tip for a couple of hours at dawn, and then sail for Serifos.'

'Serifos!' Mario exclaimed with delight. 'Good.'

'Why?' Fletcher asked.

'I will be able to see my cousin again,' Mario explained. 'He has a small hotel in the town. I have not seen him for a long time.'

'I wonder why Serifos,' Fletcher muttered. He paid little attention to the reason Salunda had given him. He felt there was a deeper significance.

'It is popular with the tourists,' Mario said, 'especially on carnival night. That is some night, Stefan.'

'I know,' Fletcher replied thoughtfully.

He leant against the wheel-house. The island was no different from many others. It had its share of antiquities and legends with the temple remains, the monastery, and the convent. It also had a number of grottoes and ancient mine workings, a relic from the days when the Venetians used to mine the island for silver. Was it also being used as a meeting-place or a hiding-place? he wondered. There had to be some hidden reason for the trip or Salunda would not have employed them. She would have used the regular ferry service. He sighed and made himself comfortable on the deck. The next twenty-four hours were going to prove very interesting in one way or another.

The following morning when Salunda appeared on deck, the *Tonos* was stationary. A slight haze hung over the crystal clear blue water. Fletcher and Mario were fishing. She frowned when she saw them at their work.

'You were hired to take me to Serifos, not to fish,' she fumed.

Fletcher looked at her patiently.

'We are only a few kilometres away from Serifos,' he said. 'But if you would care to look over the port side you will see a naval frigate watching us from a distance. We are supposed to be fishermen, so we fish. It saves a lot of bother.'

She looked at the frigate on the horizon.

'Why should they be interested in you?'

'They are interested in any vessel in the area. They have a suspicion that smuggling is carried out, and I don't want them to search my boat. They might find a few samples.'

He heaved in the net.

'Besides, if we are going to Serifos it would look less suspicious if we went selling fish, rather than as a couple of tourists.'

'Oh!' she said quietly. 'I see. I'm sorry.'

'It would be just as well if you kept out of the way in case they see you through their binoculars. That would certainly bring them over.'

She hurriedly returned to the saloon. At the foot of the small flight of steps she hesitated. The door, which she had previously bolted, had been opened during the night and was fastened against the bulkhead. She looked at Fletcher.

'How?' she asked, perplexed.

'I opened it,' he explained. 'There is an entrance into the saloon from the forward hold. I needed the charts. Besides, it would have got too hot.'

She coloured up and went into the saloon. Fletcher smiled, knowingly, and turned his attention back to the net.

For a further half an hour the frigate kept them under observation. Immediately it sailed out of sight they started the engines and headed for Serifos. Salunda joined them on deck and watched Mario gut the fish. She appeared more relaxed in their presence, even to the extent of making breakfast for them. It was almost as if she was enjoying the trip. But as they approached the island her attitude changed. She became stiff and formal again, and sat silently studying the coastline. Fletcher watched her from the wheelhouse and resisted the temptation to question her. Nor did he attempt to follow her when they put her ashore. So long as she didn't suspect him of being anything other than a former agent of Mattu he was getting a ringside seat – and there was always the return trip!

CHAPTER FIVE

The harbour at Serifos was a large open bay flanked by two piers. It was well patronised with an assorted collection of caiques and boats which included a small coaster. The town ran around the bay and rose up the hillside behind the front. The small, white cubed buildings, and gilt domed roofs glistened and sparkled in the brilliant sunshine. It appeared a busy little town with visitors and sightseers filling the narrow streets.

Fletcher brought the boat alongside the pier where a number of people were waiting for the fast hydrofoil ferry service to arrive from Piraeus. For a while he remained in the wheel-house, a little uncertain what to expect. He read the posters on the pier wall advertising the carnival which was to be held in two days time, and glanced at the patient group of bystanders. One of them, a drably dressed man of medium height, held his attention. Their arrival had aroused his curiosity. He got up from his seat and walked over to their boat, and studied its name painted across the bows. He then returned to his seat and wrote something on the back of a newspaper he was carrying.

Fletcher watched him thoughtfully. His actions could have been innocent, but on the other hand their visit could also be being passed on to someone else!

He turned his attention to the coaster across the bay, offloading stores on to a small boat alongside. It was unusual to see a vessel of such size in the harbour, and he wondered what had brought it to the island. He brought out his binoculars and studied it more closely. Two men stripped to the waist, were in the small boat, receiving the stores. They were both fair and bronzed. They didn't look like Greeks or Slavs, they looked more like Scandinavians – or Germans! Fletcher's interest increased. He looked at them again. One was in shorts with bare feet, but his companion was wearing long drill trousers with calf length boots! He put down his binoculars and called to Mario. They were the same type of boots he had seen standing behind his chair when he had been taken to see Lofer!

When Mario joined him he handed him the binoculars and pointed to the man in the small boat.

'Have a look at his boots, Mario,' he said. 'The man with Lofer was wearing a similar pair.'

Mario studied the scene.

'Seen them before?' Fletcher asked.

'I once took a party of geologists to Skyros,'

Mario grunted. 'They wore similar boots.'

'And so do archaeologists,' Fletcher said.

Mario looked at him.

'But are there any archaeological workings here?' he asked.

'I am not sure,' Fletcher said thoughtfully, 'but I rather think there are.'

He was thinking of Dr Sleitser!

'Well, we can always find out,' Mario said.

'I intend to,' Fletcher replied. 'You remain here until the ferry arrives and then meet me in the bar at the corner of the square. Keep an eye on that man reading his news-paper. He has been taking an unhealthy interest in our boat.'

Mario went back to his boxes of fish and Fletcher went ashore. He strolled slowly along the pier and joined the throngs of tourists who filled the streets. The prepar-ations for the carnival were in full swing. Decorations and bunting were being erected across the narrow streets, and the shops overflowed with the humorous and grotesque cardboard headgears which were to be worn by those who wished to join the procession. In the centre of the large cobbled square, a huge bonfire had been prepared, on top of which stood an empty throne waiting to receive its effigy for sacrifice. The colourful decorations had apparently whet the appetite of the townspeople and there was a feeling of excitement abroad. Shouts and cries of laughter came from the cafés and bars. The tension was mounting. It was going to be a wild night.

Fletcher felt the pulse of the town, but it didn't distract him. He had a different feeling about the place. He was sure that whatever Lofer and Salunda were organising was linked with the town. His eyes flashed about, taking everything in, and his vigil paid off. It enabled him to see Pula before he saw him! Not only did Pula's presence give Fletcher a surprise, but the man he was with sent the red lights flashing – it was the same man who had followed him from the train! One of Veti's men! They were sitting outside a café, deeply engrossed in conversation. Fletcher quickly darted into a nearby alleyway from where he could keep the two men under observation. Pula looked a little uneasy in the other man's presence. Occasionally he cast furtive glances about him, as if fearful of being observed. Their conversation also appeared one-sided. Pula was doing all the talking and he kept gesticulating with his hands. Veti's man sat stone-faced and impassive.

Fletcher watched them with a feeling of mounting concern. The Communists were not just watching from the side lines as he had hoped, they were being very active, and that could only mean trouble. Did Salunda know of this? he wondered. Or were they being taken for a ride? Pula was obviously the go-between, the link man, and the man who knew all the answers.

The two men abruptly stood up and left the café. Fletcher followed them across the square and watched them part company. The man who had followed him from the train made his way towards the pier, where the dark blue hydrofoil ferry was approaching the harbour. Pula, however, went to the shore and got into a powerful motor launch. Before the ferry had tied up, he was heading out to sea.

Fletcher watched him leave the bay and then continued his way to the north pier, where the coaster was offloading its stores. He now felt more certain than ever, that the men in the small boat were some of Lofer's men.

An open truck had arrived at the end of the pier and a big, heavily made man, with close-cropped hair, was leaning against the bonnet, watching the two men in the small boat.

Fletcher kept his distance. If the men were associated with Lofer, they had the advantage over him. They had seen his face, he hadn't seen theirs. He saw the small boat pull away from the coaster and head for the pier. The man leaning against the truck threw away the cigarette he had been smoking and went to meet them. Fletcher came as

113

close as he dared. When the boat came alongside they started transferring the stores on to the truck. The men worked silently, but when one of the larger crates failed to find its place on the truck at the first attempt the man who had been standing on the pier called out, savagely, to the other two, and told them to be careful. At the sound of his voice Fletcher got his answer. He had spoken in German! And his accent and tone had a familiar ring! He was the man who had questioned him when he had been taken to meet Lofer!

Fletcher took a last look at his features and quickly left them to their task. He didn't know what Salunda's reasons were for wanting him to visit Serifos, but she had certainly provided him with an opportunity of picking up some valuable pieces of the jig-saw. All he wanted now was the confirmation that Dr Sleitser was on the island, and he would have a shrewd idea who Herr Lofer was.

Fletcher got his confirmation from the man who ran the small bar where he went to wait for Mario. Dr Sleitser was indeed on the island. He was excavating an ancient temple, six kilometres south of the town on the coast. Fletcher learned a lot. Dr Sleitser had been engaged on the workings for over a month. He didn't like visitors, especially tourists, and his men very rarely visited the town. The cargo ship in the harbour was from Trieste, and had been a frequent visitor to the island ever since the Doctor had arrived. The stores that were being offloaded were supposed to be machine parts to help the Doctor with his workings. It all sounded very plausible and such archaeological expeditions were not uncommon. The islands were a veritable treasure trove for such men and the Americans, in particular, were constantly unearthing fresh relics of the past. But in Dr Sleitser's case, Fletcher was well aware that it provided an ideal front for other activities and, whether the Doctor liked it or not, he intended to see the workings for himself before he left the island.

In view of the man's readiness to talk, Fletcher also questioned him about the monastery and he confirmed what Salunda had told him. But he added one further piece of information which made Fletcher raise his eyebrows. The monks had not used the retreat for over three years, until a few days ago when a small party of them had suddenly arrived! It made Fletcher even more suspicious.

For where he was sitting Fletcher saw the ferry leave the harbour and wondered what was keeping Mario. But it was a further half an hour before he got the answer. When Mario joined him his face looked serious.

'That Turk who was wearing the white dinner jacket arrived on the ferry,' he said.

'Kasim!' Fletcher exclaimed. 'Was he alone?'

'Yes, and in a hurry.'

'Where did he go?'

'To a vineyard about one kilometre out of town. There is a large villa surrounded by a high brick wall. I waited several minutes, but he did not come out, so I came here.'

'Did anyone else follow him?'

'No, I am sure.'

'Good. Who owns the vineyard?'

'I do not know,' Mario replied, 'but I can find out from my cousin.'

'You do that, Mario. I want to visit a certain Dr Sleitser, but be careful. It wouldn't surprise me now if even Inspector Ikarios turned up.'

'Ikarios!'

'Yes, even him,' Fletcher said, and quickly explained about Pula's meeting with one of Veti's men and about the three Germans.

'It was very thoughtful of Salunda to send us here,' Mario chuckled when Fletcher had finished.

'Very,' Fletcher agreed, but he couldn't help feeling it hadn't only been to keep them occupied whilst she visited her uncle.

They parted company. Mario went in search of his cousin, and Fletcher slipped out of the town and headed south along the coast. He moved quickly along the road, keeping a watchful eye that the truck didn't

116

suddenly come up from behind. The last thing he wanted was to be seen by the Germans. After covering only a short distance, he came across a woman working in an olive grove. He questioned her about the archaeological workings, and she gave him a direct route which took him across country through the orchards and the rich lush countryside which bordered the sea.

The site of Dr Sleitser's workings was a large amphitheatre several hundred metres across. It was on the edge of the cliffs, facing the sea. Surrounding the amphitheatre was a post-and-wire fence. Fletcher crept under it and got himself into a position where he could observe what was going on without being seen.

At the far end of the amphitheatre the road ran into the site. It was a rough metal track, but its very existence made Fletcher curious. It had obviously not been made by the Doctor's party in such a short time.

The archaeological workings were a series of trenches which had exposed the foundations and bases of an ancient temple. Two men stood examining them. One was Dr Sleitser, the other a much smaller and younger man. Both wore khaki shirts and drill trousers and strong leather boots like those Fletcher had seen on the man in the small boat. Dr Sleitser stood erect and was gesticulating with his hands, as if explaining something to his companion. His face looked bronzed and his silvery goatee beard gave him a distinguished appearance. Fletcher watched him for a while and then turned his attention to their camp. There were only three tents, pitched close to the road, but projecting from a vertical face of the amphitheatre was a canvas covering which looked like the entrance to a cave.

Fletcher sat patiently studying the scene, but there was so little activity that he eventually became bored. He was about to leave when the truck drove into the camp. Its arrival brought another man on to the scene. He appeared at the entrance to the camp where he had been standing sentry. The truck pulled up alongside the canvas canopy, and the three men who had been in the town got out and started to lift the boxes from the truck and stack them under the canopy.

Fletcher remained for a further few minutes, but when the sentry started to stroll slowly around the perimeter fence he decided it was time to leave. Quickly he returned to the town. The camp and the workings had an innocent appearance. Even the lack of activity didn't surprise him. It was approaching the hottest time of the day. Most manual work was carried out during the early hours when it was much cooler. But what did make him suspicious was the precautions they had taken to keep out visitors, and also the absence of any heavy equipment. Various articles of mechanical plant had been standing near the tents, but not sufficient to warrant frequent visits by the coaster which was anchored in the harbour!

Mario was waiting for him on board. He had found out who owned the vineyard. It was a Syrian called Zerbib. He had come to live on the island a number of years ago, but spent a lot of time visiting. He was a popular man on the island and there was no indication of any political affiliations. Like everything else which glistened under the burning sun he appeared innocent and above reproach. But Fletcher knew the Syrians. They were mercenaries, even more so than the Greeks!

Mario had also picked up some valuable information about Dr Sleitser's camp site. During the occupation of Greece the Germans had used it as a site for one of their coastal gun batteries. It explained the metal road which ran into the site, but it also gave Fletcher food for thought for other reasons.

They left the harbour straight away and headed back to the bay where they were to meet Salunda. As they passed Dr Sleitser's camp site, Fletcher scanned the coastline with his binoculars. It was a forbidding promontory. Three needle-like rocks projected from the sea about fifty metres from the coast, and directly beneath the camp was an unusually smooth vertical rock face. Fletcher felt disappointed. He had been hoping to see a cave or some feature where a boat could come alongside. He felt certain that Dr Sleitser and Herr Lofer were one and the same person. He felt equally certain that the archaeological workings were a front, and that the camp was being used as a storage dump. But what was being stored there, and why, still remained a mystery.

CHAPTER SIX

Mario scowled when he saw the cloaked figure of a monk approach with Salunda, and retreated, pointedly, to the wheel-house. Fletcher waited on the shore. He was curious to meet the man.

Salunda came up to him. Her face looked tense.

'My uncle is returning with me,' she said seriously.

Fletcher nodded his head understandingly, and helped her aboard. He turned to help her uncle also, but the man had lithely jumped on to the deck. It was just as well, because Fletcher momentarily froze when he saw the man's face. It was Abdul Rassitz! There was no mistaking the widely spaced, deep set, brown eyes and the dark features. Fletcher's pulse quickened. He cast a furtive glance at Mario and was thankful he had his back to them. The last thing he wanted was to let Rassitz know they recognised him, and Mario could not hide his emotions.

Salunda and Rassitz disappeared into the saloon, and Fletcher joined Mario in the wheel-house. Silently he marvelled at his good fortune. Rassitz was the spearhead of trouble and he had him right there on his boat. But that was not all. He also knew where Rassitz was hiding and he had a shrewd idea where he would be on the mainland. The ball had bounced right into Fletcher's lap. He now had control of the situation. He could nip the plot in the bud if it got out of hand. But just what was Rassitz planning? he wondered. What had lured the fox into the lion's den? It was a dangerous move. If Ikarios or any of the Greek Security got wind of it, he would be a dead duck. The stakes had to be high for him to take such a gamble. Fletcher wanted to know just how high – and who was holding the pot.

He decided against confiding in Mario at the moment. He didn't want anything to arouse Rassitz' suspicions.

Salunda appeared on deck, and he went over to her. She still looked tense and on edge.

'And what did you see in Serifos?' she asked.

Fletcher looked at her. Was she really interested? Or was she putting on an act?

'A town preparing for a carnival,' he said flatly, 'and a small coaster offloading stores.'

She said nothing.

'The stores were being collected by three Germans. They went to Dr Sleitser's camp.' He paused then added: 'Herr Lofer was also a German.'

'You are very observant indeed,' she said quietly.

He looked her full in the face.

'Very,' he said.

She dropped his eyes.

'What else did you see?' she asked.

Fletcher hesitated. He didn't intend to tell her about Pula, but she would find out about Kasim's visit.

'The Turk who was with you last night, wearing the dinner jacket,' he said.

'Kasim,' she explained.

'He arrived by ferry.'

'Kasim!' she whispered hoarsely. 'The fool!'

The news had shaken her. Her brow became furrowed, her eyes worried.

'Where did he go to?' she asked desperately.

Fletcher shrugged.

'I do not know,' he lied, 'but I shouldn't worry. There is a ferry back to Piraeus later this evening. He will probably return with it.'

The information seemed to ease her mind a little, but she didn't discuss it further.

'My uncle and I are to meet Ahmad tonight on the mainland at the same bay where I joined you. If all goes well you might get a bonus.'

She turned abruptly, and went back to the cabin and Rassitz.

Fletcher discussed their course with Mario

and then settled himself on deck. He felt disappointed with Salunda. Rassitz was a fanatic bent on stirring up trouble. If Salunda was one of his disciples she was not the woman he had hoped. He quickly shrugged off this feeling. In this type of business there was no place for personal emotions.

For the remainder of the afternoon Fletcher sat on the deck watching the coastline of the small islands through his binoculars. He was still doing this when Salunda joined him again.

'My uncle is asleep,' she explained.

Fletcher put down the binoculars, surprised at her presence.

'Which island is that?' she asked.

'Kithnos,' he said, 'and those white buildings you can see are the ruins of an old Venetian fortress. There used to be a town on the island a long time ago.'

He handed her the binoculars.

'It looks very beautiful,' she said wistfully.

'Yes,' he agreed. 'All the islands are beautiful.' He sighed, and looked at the calm blue sea, and the green island. 'It is so peaceful and beautiful here that you wonder how the world can go so wrong.'

'You are a strange man, Fettos,' she said, 'for a...'

She didn't finish her sentence.

'Gun-runner? Smuggler? Mercenary?' Fletcher asked.

She flushed up, but said nothing.

'Why?' Fletcher asked. 'Because I like the islands? Or because I am a philosopher? All sailors are philosophers.'

'I love my island, also,' she said evading his question.

She was referring to Cyprus, Fletcher thought, but he didn't question her about it.

'How many languages can you speak?' she asked suddenly, changing the subject.

The question took Fletcher by surprise.

'Oh, Greek, Turkish and a smattering of Arabic,' he said.

'And English!' she added.

He turned to look at her. Their eyes met, but she looked away.

'I am sorry,' she apologised. 'I didn't mean to pry. I saw a book, this morning. When I was preparing the breakfast.'

Fletcher mentally cursed himself. He had no right to leave an English book in his cabin. Desperately, he wondered if she suspected him. But she had found the book that morning and Rassitz had still come with her. He would never have done that if there had been any suspicions.

'I can speak a little English,' he said calmly. 'In my business you have to be able to converse with all nationalities. It is also good for the tourists. I got that book from an English schoolteacher last year. She said it would improve my vocabulary.'

She appeared to accept his explanation.

'Where do you live, Fettos?' she asked.

'In a small village on the island of Chios. It is very much like that island.'

She looked pensively at the picturesque coastline.

'Why do you lead this kind of life?'

'To pay for the boat,' he replied. 'It cost Mario and me a lot of money. Soon it will be ours.'

'What will you do then?'

'Fish, and sail the islands.'

Her questioning puzzled him. He felt it was leading up to something.

'Are you married?' she asked abruptly.

Fletcher smiled. 'Unfortunately, no.'

'Where will you go after we leave you?'

'Back to Piraeus.'

'Don't,' she said hurriedly. 'Don't, Fettos. Go back home.'

There was a note of concern in her voice.

He turned to face her. She was trying to tell him something. He put his hand on her arm. She didn't resist his action. In fact she came closer.

'Why, Salunda?' he asked tenderly. 'Why?'

She opened her mouth to say something and hesitated.

'Karima!' A high pitched screaming voice called out from the well of the saloon. 'Karima!'

It was Rassitz!

Salunda stood up abruptly. The spell was broken. Whatever she was going to say remained unsaid. She rushed back to the cabin and the door was slammed and bolted.

'Rassitz!' Mario hissed. 'That bastard!'

He spat, demonstratively, over the side of the boat. When he re-entered the wheelhouse, he brought out his dagger and stuck it forcibly into the woodwork.

'Stefan,' he said. 'We kill him.'

Fletcher came up beside him.

'No, Mario,' he said quietly. 'No.'

Mario looked at him with disgust.

'He is a snake. He will cause trouble.'

'If we kill him,' Fletcher whispered, 'it will make a martyr out of him. They would find out who did it, and it would be very embarrassing for our friends in London. We cannot afford that. We must watch him and see what he is up to.' He paused dramatically. 'If at the last moment he has an accident that does not involve my friends, that is another matter.'

Mario silently put his dagger away and brought the boat back on its course. He had got the message.

Fletcher only saw Salunda again once on the trip back to the mainland, and that was when she and Rassitz left the boat. Ahmad was waiting for them. He handed the money over to Fletcher, and rushed Salunda and Rassitz away from the beach.

Thoughtfully, Fletcher turned the boat out to sea again and headed for Piraeus.

'She was trying to warn you,' Mario said, lighting a small cigarillo.

Fletcher was well aware of this and he was already making plans.

'Mario,' he said cheerfully, 'tonight we have some money, so let us celebrate. First, I must call and see my banker in Athens, and then we will enjoy ourselves.'

Mario looked at him understandingly.

'Sure, Stefan,' he said. 'Tonight we will celebrate.'

After anchoring the boat in the harbour, Fletcher hurried into Athens. It was imperative that he passed on the news of Rassitz' whereabouts to Spencer. He phoned Spencer from the station and in a cryptic telephone conversation learned that Spencer was unable to leave his house. Undaunted, Fletcher promised to deliver the goods personally. He left the telephone kiosk and picked up Toni. For a few minutes they toured the town making absolutely certain they weren't being followed and then Fletcher directed him to Spencer's house. Whilst Toni remained on watch outside the grounds, Fletcher slipped through the shrubbery and entered the open french window of the study. He closed the window behind him and pulled the curtains. A few seconds later Spencer entered the room. He was wearing evening dress.

'You'll have to be quick,' he said. 'I'm entertaining. Help yourself to a drink.'

Fletcher poured out a stiff whisky. It had been a long day.

'Rassitz has arrived,' he said.

'Where?' Spencer asked.

'In Athens,' Fletcher said.

Spencer looked at him sharply.

'How do you know?'

'Because I brought him.'

'You what?' Spencer exploded.

'I brought him this afternoon from Serifos where he has been hiding in a monastery.'

'Where is he now?'

'At the Villa Acancia.'

'Bah!' Spencer growled. 'Turkish Embassy. We can't touch him there.'

'You can't, but I can,' Fletcher mused. 'But it's too early. There is more to it than just Rassitz.'

'Such as?'

'The Communists are involved!'

Spencer frowned.

'Wait here,' he said. 'I will be back.'

He left the room, but returned in a few minutes.

'Let's have the full story,' he said, and poured himself a drink.

Fletcher related everything that had taken place since the last time they had met. How he had been taken to see Lofer. Of his visit to Pula's surgery and his trip to Serifos.

'So you think Dr Sleitser and Lofer are the same person?' Spencer asked when Fletcher had finished.

'Yes,' Fletcher said. 'I feel certain.'

'Leave that one with me,' Spencer said thoughtfully. 'I'll know all about Dr Sleitser within twelve hours.'

'What about Veti?' Fletcher asked.

Spencer played with his glass.

'The Russians are not involved,' he said finally. 'Of that I am certain. Veti is either employed by the Albanians, or he is playing a lone hand.'

Fletcher shook his head.

'They don't permit that,' he said, 'everything Veti does is controlled by the K.G.B. If he is not being directed from the Kremlin, then it must be from some other Communist country.'

'In that case it will definitely be the Albanians. Grevosky is hardly likely to warn me about Lofer if they are using him.'

'But why warn you at all?' Fletcher asked.

Spencer smiled.

'China, old boy. Quite simply China. Albania and China are friends. Russia and China are not. So to get one over on the Chinese they put a spoke in the Albanian's wheels. At the same time we owe them a favour.'

'Well, it doesn't make my job any easier,' Fletcher said. 'Russians or Albanians, they are all the same.'

'Yes,' Spencer agreed seriously. 'You will have to watch your step. What do you think they are up to?'

'Supplying weapons to Rassitz.'

'The Turks can supply their own and they don't normally deal with the Communists.'

'That's what puzzles me,' Fletcher said. 'But supposing Rassitz is unaware that the Communists are at the back of this. Pula is obviously the middle man. They have nothing to link him with Veti.'

'You did.'

'Only because I happen to know some of Veti's men. But I doubt if Rassitz does, or any of the Turks in Athens.'

'But we still don't know what they are supplying to Rassitz.'

'No,' Fletcher agreed. 'If anything. It may only be money, or information.'

'Until we know what it is all about, there is nothing we can do.'

Fletcher sighed. There were times when he wished he had some other form of occupation. There was no comfort in his job. He glanced at the rows of books. How he would have liked to spend the evening in the high-backed chair reading any one of them, with a bottle of Scotch as his companion. He finished off his drink and stood up.

'I'll be in touch as soon as I know anything,' he said.

Spencer frowned.

'Tomorrow I have to go with the Ambassador to Rhodes, but I shall be back in the evening.'

'Well, I will try and keep all the parties quiet during the day so you can enjoy your trip.'

Spencer growled.

'I would swop you jobs any day,' he grunted.

Fletcher was about to give a suitable retort when there was an impatient tapping on the door. Spencer's wife called out in an irritated tone.

'No thanks,' Fletcher smiled. 'It does have certain advantages, I agree.'

He left Spencer to pacify his wife, and returned to the taxi. For a while he allowed Toni to drive aimlessly around the town whilst he determined what to do. Finally, he decided to call and see Pula. He had a shrewd idea what the man was up to, and he also had a fair idea of his character. With a bit of persuasion, he reckoned he could make Pula talk. But it was a fruitless journey. There was no sign of Pula in his apartment, or his surgery.

Fletcher then returned to Piraeus. Standing parked near his apartment was the cream Mercedes with two of Veti's strongarm men sitting like two stuffed dummies. With an unusual lack of concern he ignored their presence and joined Mario in the Metropol Bar close to the harbour. It was a large, noisy room, with a cosmopolitan gathering of customers, all bent on various forms of revelry. Mario was already in high spirits when Fletcher arrived, and as the night wore on his exuberance became more volatile. Fletcher was also in fine form, but the lack of sleep and the harsh treatment he had received at the hands of Lofer's men began to tell. Shortly before midnight he retired, and staggered back to his apartment.

About an hour later the apartment door noiselessly opened and the dark figure of a man slipped into the room. After closing the door behind him he stealthily moved into the bedroom and saw the still form lying on the bed. He stopped at the foot of the bed, and with the quick flashing movement of an expert, projected a narrow pointed dagger from his sleeve into the form on the bed. The dagger sank into the figure without causing a stir, and the man moved forward, surprised at the lack of reaction received by his lethal weapon. As he did so, Fletcher hit him from behind, with a deft, sharp, karate blow, and the man sank to the floor. Fletcher dragged him out of the bedroom as Mario entered the apartment.

'He followed you from the Metropol,' Mario snarled.

'Do you recognise him?' Fletcher asked.

Mario came over to look at the body and Fletcher turned to switch on the electric light. As he did so, he saw the nozzle of a revolver pointing at them through the slits of the louvred balcony door!

'Down Mario!' he yelled. 'Down!' Frantically he pulled Mario with him to the floor, as two sharp cracks spurted from the revolver. There was a thud, thud, as the bullets found a home, but Fletcher wasn't hit, and, as he scrambled into the adjoining room, he heard Mario scurry towards the entrance lobby. Fletcher glanced at the still body of his would-be murderer and saw two bloody patches on his chest. In a flash he realised who the gunman had been after, and he dashed over to the balcony doors. Without stopping, he jumped into the bushes and brushed his way through the shrubbery to the roadway. But he was too late. The boulevard was deserted. Even the Mercedes had gone! He glanced back at the apartment building. There was no sign of any commotion, the block was still in darkness.

Thoughtfully he retraced his steps. The man on the balcony had shot the assassin because it was the easiest way out. It was unlikely he would have killed both Fletcher and Mario, and that would have left one of them to make the man talk. But who was in such a hurry to get rid of him? Was it Rassitz? Was he covering up his traces? Salunda had certainly tried to warn him against some danger. Was this it? But the man didn't look like a Turk and it was unlike them to hire a Greek. And if it wasn't Rassitz, who else could it be? Verti perhaps? He wondered about Verti. Was Fletcher's presence beginning to trouble him? The Mercedes had long since disappeared. Was that significant? Or were they only keeping a watch on him during normal working hours? It had to be one or the other, and Fletcher knew who would give him the answer – Salunda!

'We won't get anything out of him,' Mario said when Fletcher joined him. 'He's dead.'

Fletcher looked at the dead man's face. It was like many others which hung around the harbour bars – rough, dark and weather beaten.

'Local?' he asked.

Mario shook his head and opened the man's thick gnarled hands.

'No,' he said. 'He's from the mountains. Probably Crete.'

'Why bring in a stranger?' Fletcher asked. 'There are plenty of locals who would have done the job.'

'They could become an embarrassment,' Mario said. 'This one would be out of the way altogether.'

Fletcher grunted. Mario could be right. In which case it sounded more like Verti's work than Rassitz', but he would reserve his judgement until he had spoken to Salunda.

'What do we do with him?' Mario asked.

'Get rid of him,' Fletcher replied, 'and quick, before we have any more visitors.'

They got a towel and wrapped it around the dead man's chest. Mario went to fetch the car, and Fletcher dragged the body through the shrubs to the roadway. Fortunately the boulevard was still deserted, but the town would not be, and a dead body was not the ideal companion to be seen with. They bundled the body into the rear seat of the car and drove swiftly through the moonlit streets. When they reached the east end of the town they drove into a ship-building yard, and quickly dumped the body in a conspicuous place where it would be seen before the sun got at it.

It was in a more relaxed atmosphere that they drove back to the apartment. Fletcher was beginning to trouble someone, that was a good sign. But whoever they were, they wouldn't give up after one abortive attempt. They would try again, and the next time they would be even more determined.

'The apartment is becoming too well known,' Fletcher said seriously. 'I think we will only operate from the boat from now on.'

Mario agreed. Like Fletcher he felt safer in the middle of the harbour.

'We'll collect my belongings, and you take

136

them aboard the *Tonos,* whilst I go into Athena.'

Mario looked at him.

'Is it wise to go alone?' he asked.

Fletcher shrugged. It was a risk he was prepared to take. He wanted to get clear of the apartment and he also wanted to know who was wanting him out of the way. Until he achieved both he wouldn't feel happy.

CHAPTER SEVEN

Fletcher saw Inspector Ikarios as he was getting out of the car and immediately felt the full blast of his icy tones.

'Good evening, Fettos. You appear to have inherited some money since last we met,' the Inspector sneered. He was not alone. His big burly Sergeant was with him, and another similarly built policeman hovered in the background.

'Search the car,' the Inspector snapped.

'What do you hope to find?' Fletcher growled as the Sergeant and the other policeman started their search.

The Inspector didn't reply. He was looking at Fletcher and Mario in turn, a sadistic smile on his face.

'Where have you been?' he barked at Mario.

Mario shrugged and took his time in answering.

'Celebrating,' he said.

'Where?'

Mario purposely lit a cigarette and blew smoke dangerously close to the Inspector's face.

'Metropol,' he said.

The Inspector turned to Fletcher.

'And how can you afford to run a car and rent a luxury apartment when only five days ago you had no money?'

But Fletcher wasn't in the mood to play cat and mouse with him. He knew Ikarios. No matter what they said they would end up in the police station. There was that look in the Inspector's eye which forecast a long tough night, and Fletcher had other plans.

'What the hell has it got to do with you?' he asked angrily.

The Inspector's face looked like thunder.

'I'll tell you what it has to do with me, Fettos,' he hissed. 'Someone reported a shooting. They heard shots coming from an apartment on the ground floor – your apartment! And if I find any evidence to confirm it, I am going to take you apart.'

Mario pointedly blew a cloud of smoke into the Inspector's face.

'Find anything?' Ikarios asked impatiently.

The Sergeant shook his head.

'Let's have a look inside then,' the Inspector snapped. 'Get going.'

Fletcher looked at the Sergeant and his assistant. They were watching them like two hawks, waiting to see which way they moved. It wasn't the ideal moment to make a break for it. He shrugged, and led the way into the apartment, but he didn't hold out much hope. Ikarios would find the bloodstains, he was in that kind of mood.

When they entered the apartment, however, Fletcher had more to worry about than bloodstains. Sitting facing them in the basket chair was Kasim! But he wasn't going to say much – he was dead! His head lolled on one side indicating a broken neck!

Ikarios gave a delighted cry and the Sergeant brandished his automatic.

'Get against the wall,' the Sergeant snarled, 'and keep your hands up.'

Fletcher looked at the dead Kasim. He had wondered who had phoned the Inspector – now he knew. It was the same person who had put Kasim's body in the basket chair!– The same person who had shot the Cretan!

He watched the Inspector touch the Turk, and the body fell forward on to the floor. The last time they had seen Kasim was in Serifos. Had he returned from the island dead or alive? he wondered. Was this Lofer's work? Or Veti's?

'Who is he?' Ikarios asked.

Fletcher looked blank.

'No idea,' he lied.

The Inspector pierced his eyes.

'You would help yourself more if you co-operated,' he said. 'He is in your apartment.'

'Would I have come back if I had known he was here?' Fletcher asked.

'Yes,' Ikarios snapped. 'To get rid of him.'

141

'He has been dead for hours,' Mario grunted.

'How do you know?'

'He's as stiff as a board,' Mario said.

Ikarios examined the body again, and then ordered the policeman to phone for an ambulance.

There were only two of them now, Fletcher thought. If they were going to make a break for it, it had to be now, before the other policeman returned. He glanced meaningly at Mario. Mario understood, and moved that fraction closer to the inspector who was examining the contents of Kasim's pockets.

'Look, Sergeant, must we stand like this?' Fletcher asked, and moved towards the burly policeman.

'Get back,' the Sergeant snarled, and put out his arm to push him against the wall. It was just what Fletcher had hoped he would do. In a flash he had knocked the man's arm away, and with a lightning stroke, he smacked the side of his other hand into the Sergeant's neck. As the policeman doubled up, choking for breath, Fletcher crashed his knee into the man's jaw and sent him reeling. Mario moved with equal speed, and before the Inspector had time to get his revolver out of his pocket Mario had landed on top of him like a pouncing tiger. The Inspector's head crashed onto the floor and he didn't move. Almost with disgust Mario stood up. He saw

142

the other policeman appear at the door and dived towards him. The policeman's revolver spurted fire as Mario hit him, and a bullet ricocheted off the concrete ceiling. Fletcher kicked the revolver away from the policeman's hand, and Mario put the final touches to rendering him harmless.

Fletcher ran out to the car and started the engine.

'Get back to the boat,' he yelled to Mario. 'Meet me at Kimo Bay.'

Mario didn't waste time discussing the matter. He had to get the boat out of the harbour before the Inspector put in his alert. Fletcher drove out of Piraeus with the same amount of urgency. In Athens he quickly ditched the car and went by foot to where Toni parked his taxi. Fortunately Toni was in his cab, asleep across the front seat.

'Athena,' Fletcher said, 'quickly.'

Toni didn't need any second bidding. The urgency in Fletcher's voice, and the timing of his arrival was clear enough indication that it wasn't a sight-seeing trip.

In Athena Fletcher directed him to the Villa Acancia.

'Don't park,' Fletcher said, as he got out. 'It might attract attention. Give me thirty minutes, then come back and tour the block. If I haven't turned up within the hour go and met Mario at Kimo Bay. Tell him to contact our friends. They will know what to do.'

When the taxi was out of sight, Fletcher scaled the high brick wall and landed in the garden which surrounded the residence. Despite the lateness of the hour there were still a number of lights on in the main building and the annexe. Cautiously he moved forward. He would have to be quick. It would soon be dawn and he wanted to get back to Mario so that they could hide the boat where Ikarios wouldn't find them.

As he approached the annexe, he saw a man strolling around the grounds. He looked bored and tired. Fletcher picked up a loose stone from the ground and got into a position where he could dispense with him quietly and efficiently. As the man strolled past, he hit him from behind. Before he landed on the ground, Fletcher had grabbed him around the waist, and dragged him into the bushes.

A light was shining from the large room Fletcher had been in the previous evening, but it was empty. The room next to it, however, was occupied, but the louvred shutters were fastened over the window. Fletcher brought out his knife and deftly cut a small hole in the woodwork.

In the room were four men. One was Rassitz, another Ahmad, but the remaining two were strangers. One of these was sitting away from the other three men, and he held Fletcher's attention. He looked like a Greek, and a business man. His hair was sleek black, his face olive and heavily jowled. He was wearing a plain grey sports shirt and a silk tie. His hands rested on the table, displaying a number of gold rings. Fletcher looked at his face again. He had never seen it before, but there was something about him which appeared familiar. At the other end of the table sat the three Turks, Rassitz, Ahmad and the third man – a tall, lean, sallow-faced man, who sat staring at the Greek.

The Greek was doing all the talking, but his voice was cushioned by the double-glazed window.

Fletcher moved away. It wasn't these men that he had come to see. The adjoining room was a bedroom but it wasn't occupied. Two subsequent rooms were also empty. With mounting impatience, he moved around the building. It was with a feeling of relief that he eventually found what he had been looking for – Salunda's room! He saw her still figure under a mosquito net. He crept into the room and pulled back the net. As he did so, she awoke. Quickly, he put his hand over her mouth. There was a look of horror on her face, as if she had seen a ghost.

Slowly he removed his hand.

'You!' she gasped. 'I thought you were…'

'Dead?' Fletcher asked, completing the sentence for her.

She pulled a sheet around her.

'They will kill you,' she whispered desperately, 'you must go before they find you.'

'I want some answers first,' he said quietly, but firmly.

'Please go,' she pleaded.

'Who hired that dago to murder me?' he asked grimly.

She looked at him, a frightened expression on her face, but she didn't answer. Her silence was pointed. It was Rassitz after all, he thought.

He tried another tack.

'Who is that man with Rassitz?'

'Oh! I don't know,' she cried. 'Please go.'

But Fletcher wanted information. He hadn't intended to tell her about Kasim, but it was going to be the only way to get her to talk.

'Look, Salunda,' he whispered urgently, 'I don't know what your game is, but you are in danger.' He paused. 'Kasim is dead.'

She gave a stifled cry, and Fletcher quickly put his hand gently over her mouth. He could feel her shaking as she tried to control her emotions.

'I am very sorry,' he said.

He waited patiently for her to get over the shock.

'Why did Kasim go to Serifos?' he asked.

She looked at him pleadingly. There were tears in her eyes.

'He didn't trust Rassitz,' she murmured.

146

'Why not?' Fletcher asked.

'Because of Kronos,' she said quietly. She had got a grip of herself. 'Kasim employed Kronos to watch developments on Serifos. We got a message from him saying he had found out something of importance. Unfortunately, he was killed before we talked to him.'

'But why did he suspect Rassitz?' Fletcher insisted.

'Everything fitted too neatly,' she said. 'We thought he was being used.'

'The Communists?' Fletcher asked.

'I don't know,' she half cried.

'Why did Kasim go to the Syrian's house?'

'It is to be used as a meeting place.'

'What is happening on Serifos?'

She hesitated.

'Oh, please go,' she pleaded. 'There is nothing you can do now.'

'But there is,' Fletcher quickly replied. 'What is happening?'

'Dr Sleitser has a shipment of arms. There is a cave below his camp. He has a boat there, ready to take Rassitz and his men to Cyprus.'

'When?' Fletcher asked.

'Tonight, during the carnival.'

'What is so special about this shipment?' Fletcher asked.

'I don't know,' she said dejectedly. 'We never found out. My father was not told.

147

That is why Kasim and I came here.'

Father? Fletcher looked at her sharply. Who was her father? A shout from the gardens stopped him from asking. He hadn't hit the sentry hard enough!

Salunda looked frightened again.

'Please go,' she cried. 'Please!'

Fletcher hesitated. There was a lot more he wanted to know, but he valued his life. An impatient banging on the door settled the matter. He slipped out of the net and quickly scrambled through the window. As he darted into the bushes a Turk appeared on the veranda waving an automatic. A shot rang out, but the bullet went wide of its target. Fletcher crashed his way towards the boundary wall. Behind him lights flashed and voices shouted out orders. As he climbed the wall they saw him, and another shot rang out. This time the bullet smacked into the brickwork perilously close to his body. Frantically he flung himself over the obstacle and landed on the roadway. Swiftly he raced through the deserted streets until he was well clear of the area. When he was satisfied that he was not being followed, he cautiously retraced his steps until he found Toni. Gladly he slunk into the rear seat of the taxi and collected his thoughts together. He hadn't got all the answers from Salunda that he had hoped, but he had learned sufficient to realise that the next twenty-four hours were going to be

148

crucial. They had to stop Rassitz from getting to Cyprus at all costs. It would mean sailing from Serifos during daylight, but it was a risk they would have to take. He also intended to stick his neck out even further and visit Pula. He was the one man who knew all the answers, and Fletcher still had a lot of questions to ask.

Dawn was breaking as Toni drove into Kimo Bay. Fletcher could see Mario standing on the deck of the *Tonos* anxiously waiting for him. He quickly arranged to meet Toni again during the heat of the day and hurried aboard. Mario immediately took the *Tonos* out to sea and along the rocky coastline until he found a small inlet, where an overhanging cliff provided a measure of camouflage. Only then did he question Fletcher.

'What do we do now?' he asked.

'We go back to Serifos,' Fletcher replied. 'Dr Sleitser has a boat near his camp loaded with arms, ready to take Rassitz and his party to Cyprus.'

'Rassitz,' Mario snarled. 'We should have killed him as I said.'

'Patience, Mario. There is still time, if necessary. Sleitser and Lofer are the same person, so that is no mystery now. What we don't know is where Veti fits into the picture.'

'He is up to no good whatever he is doing,' Mario mumbled.

'That's what worries me,' Fletcher said.

'They may even be supplying the shipment. In which case I have a feeling that Rassitz is not aware of this. Pula has been the middle man in the whole business.'

'Then why don't we visit Pula before we go to Serifos?'

'I intend to,' Fletcher said. 'I have arranged to meet Toni at midday.'

'I will come with you,' Mario said eagerly. 'I would like to meet this spider, Pula.'

'No, Mario, you must stay with the boat.'

Mario grunted his disapproval, but Fletcher had made up his mind. He could handle Pula on his own.

'We had better get some rest,' Fletcher said. 'It is going to be another long night.'

'But interesting?' Mario asked hopefully.

'I don't think you will be disappointed,' Fletcher said, and added thoughtfully: 'Have you ever worked for Veti?'

'Yes,' Mario said. 'I did a small job for him last year.' He didn't say what the job was. 'Why?'

'Have you ever met him?'

Mario shook his head. 'No,' he said. 'He always operates through one of his men.'

'Always?' Fletcher asked.

'At my level, yes.'

'You wouldn't recognise him?'

'No.'

'Pity,' Fletcher muttered. He had suddenly developed certain nagging suspicions, and if they were correct it made it all the more vital to talk with Pula and stop Rassitz reaching Cyprus. But there was nothing he could do until later that day, and he went below to catch up on his sleep.

Toni arrived punctually at midday and drove Fletcher into Athens. Fletcher had selected the time purposely, because it was the part of the day when the fierce sun drove most people indoors, and Pula would not be working. There was no sign of the Mercedes, or any police car, in the boulevard outside Pula's apartment block, but as a precaution Fletcher entered the building from a rear entrance. He took the lift to the fifth floor and hopefully rang the bell to Pula's apartment. But Pula was not at home. He tried the surgery door. This was locked, but through the glass panel he saw the receptionist approach and unfasten the lock.

'Is Mr Pula in?' Fletcher asked.

'No,' the girl replied. 'He hasn't been here all day.'

There was a note of concern in her voice which made Fletcher curious.

'Were you expecting him?' he asked.

'Yes. He had a number of important patients visiting him today.'

'Who?' Fletcher asked.

The girl looked confused.

'I am not allowed to say,' she mumbled.

Fletcher brushed past her, and, ignoring

her protests, opened the dentist's appointment book. One name held his attention – A. Zonakas! His name on the page didn't make Fletcher's mind any easier.

'Did this man turn up?' he asked pointing to Zonakas' name.

She looked blank.

'Did he?' he asked sharply.

'Yes,' she said, startled by his tone.

'When did you last see Mr Pula?'

'Yesterday afternoon. He had been away all morning on his boat. He attended to some patients, but he went out again about 6 p.m.'

'Did you try his apartment, this morning?'

She blushed and turned her head away. Fletcher understood. She was not only Pula's receptionist!

'So Pula hasn't been seen since 6 p.m., last night,' he muttered thoughtfully. Either somebody had got to him before he could be made to talk, or he had got himself out of the way until the deal was completed. Somehow Fletcher felt it was the former.

'I wouldn't wait too long for him,' he said meaningly. 'In fact, I would 'phone the police.'

Back in the taxi Fletcher wondered what to do next. It would be like looking for a needle in a haystack trying to locate Pula, supposing he was still alive. Even his boat was like hundreds of others. But the sands were running

152

out fast and he hadn't got all the answers. He had to make some quick decisions and get to Serifos. He cursed Spencer for being in Rhodes and decided to risk going into Inspector Ikarios' own territory in Piraeus. His friend, the Patriarch, could be relied upon to pass on any messages, and he was above suspicion.

CHAPTER EIGHT

Long before Fletcher and Mario reached Serifos, they saw signs that the carnival was well under way. Rockets and flares pierced the sky and a red glow hung over the town. As they entered the bay the sound of music and merriment carried out across the water. The harbour was packed with a variety of boats, all gaily decorated, and the only berth Fletcher could find was alongside the south pier. It was at the wrong end of the town for what Fletcher had in mind, but it allowed them to go ashore unnoticed.

'Seems like one hell of a party,' Mario grunted.

Fletcher agreed. Whatever religious motives had once initiated the carnival belonged to history. It had now become an excuse to give vent to emotions which were being stifled during the long hot days of summer. The town looked as if it had gone wild. Bizarre, grotesque, ludicrous figures bobbed about amidst a colourful display of costumes which swirled and moved in rhythm with fast, pulsating music, which blared from the loudspeakers.

But the crowded streets provided an ideal

camouflage for Rassitz and his party to gather and sail for Cyprus. They would be slipping into the town from far and near.

'It is still early yet,' Fletcher said. 'Rassitz and his party will be arriving in ones and twos. They will be meeting at the Syrian's house.'

'Where will they sail from?' Mario asked.

'Dr Sleitser has his boat hidden in a cave near his camp. That's where they will make for, but they won't leave until all the ferry boats start leaving the harbour.'

'So we stop Rassitz getting to the camp?' Mario asked.

'There are too many for that,' Fletcher replied. 'But we must stop Salunda. Somehow we have to get her away from the rest of them.'

'But what about Rassitz?' Mario growled.

'Don't worry, Mario, I haven't forgotten about him.' Fletcher didn't enlarge upon his statement and Mario didn't question him further. He had worked with Fletcher long enough to know that Fletcher would not let Rassitz slip through his fingers.

'That's interesting,' Fletcher said.

'What?' Mario asked.

'See what has joined the fleet?'

Mario turned and looked across the bay. Another boat had appeared, but it wasn't lit up like the rest.

'The frigate?' Mario asked.

'Looks like it,' Fletcher said. 'I wonder what brings her here?' He didn't wait for an answer. 'Let's get going,' he said. 'We'll make our way through the town and meet on the road to Zerbib's house, at the first olive grove.'

Fletcher went first. He hadn't any idea what he was going to do, but he was determined to stop Salunda from being taken to Dr Sleitser's camp. When he joined the road which ran around the harbour, he had to almost fight his way through the throngs of people bent on making the most of the night. On several occasions he was grabbed and enticed to join in with the dancing. Eventually he reached the square where the crowd was even thicker. They surged and chanted as they waited for the bonfire to be lit and the procession to begin. Again Fletcher forced his way through the barrier. When he was half-way across the saw two men appear on a nearby hotel balcony. He recongised them immediately. It was Inspector Ikarios and his sergeant! They stood watching the scene from their vantage point. Desperately Fletcher joined a nearby group of revellers. The last thing he wanted was to be seen by the Inspector. There wasn't time for explanations, even if the Inspector was prepared to listen. From the corner of his eye he watched the two men. He saw the Sergeant point out to sea. What had brought them here? he wondered. Kasim? Or was the Inspector also on to Rassitz? Was that why the frigate was anchored off the bay? He saw the Inspector abruptly turn and leave the balcony followed by the Sergeant, and he stopped questioning their presence. More than ever, he felt that he now had to get out of the town and find Salunda. With renewed determination he forced his way through the crowd. But the road out of the town was at the north end of the bay and he still had part of the harbour front to negotiate. He had almost reached his objective when two figures wearing carnival headgear jolted roughly against him. Patiently he tried to push them out of the way, but they hovered over him. He felt something jab into his side. He looked to see what it was, and saw the muzzle of a revolver fitted with a silencer pointing at him! At the same instant a pair of hands roughly grabbed his arm.

'No trouble or we kill you,' a voice hissed from behind the headgear.

They were right on top of him. Two stupid-looking figures. For a fleeting moment he contemplated making a break for it, but the silencer decided him against it. They would shoot him and no one would hear. He would become another over-jubilant visitor who had had too much to drink.

He allowed himself to be pushed along the front and through the curtained opening of a small shop. The room was in darkness, except for the reflected light from the street. At one end was a small counter displaying various grocery goods, but at the other stood a man staring out through a window towards the brilliantly lit pier. He had his back to Fletcher, but his sleek black hair and plain grey, cotton shirt looked familiar. He continued to stare out of the window, unconcerned at Fletcher's arrival.

The two men who had brought Fletcher took off their headgear. One of them was the man who had followed Fletcher from the train!– One of Veti's men! The man at the window turned and looked at Fletcher. There was no need to introduce himself, Fletcher knew who he was – Veti! But Fletcher also recognised him as the man who had been talking to Rassitz at the Villa Acancia the previous evening!

'Where is the other one?' Veti asked in a soft, but crisp voice.

'Rafel is looking for him,' one of the men replied.

Veti nodded his head understandingly, and motioned the man to take his place at the window. Fletcher could guess who they were expecting. The other man stood near the curtain opening, a revolver in his hand. Veti sat down on a small stool. He flicked his fingers and a similar seat was produced for Fletcher.

'Good evening, Fettos,' Veti said. 'I have wondered when we would eventually meet.'

Fletcher glanced around the drab room and at the man pointing the automatic at him.

'Not quite what I expected of you,' he said.

Veti shrugged.

'In our business, Fettos, it is all a matter of timing. Since you decided to visit Serifos on this particular evening, I can only offer you this. If it had been in Piraeus it would have been more comfortable.'

'I am surprised you thought it necessary for us to meet at all,' Fletcher remarked.

Veti made a despairing gesture with his hands.

'Unfortunately your presence tonight could interfere with my plans, and if that happened my principals would be most upset.'

'And just who are your principals this time?' Fletcher asked. 'The Russians or the Albanians?'

'Does it matter?' Veti retorted.

'Purely academic,' Fletcher said. 'It surprises me that you are interested at all. One can hardly think that Rassitz shares your doctrines.'

'We aren't trying to convert him,' Veti remarked dryly. 'Only to use him.'

'For what purpose?' Fletcher asked.

Veti smiled. 'Let us stop being naïve, Fettos.

We are well aware of your Rhodes Conference next month. Need I say more?'

No, Fletcher thought. There was no need to spell it out; he knew the rest. An armed Rassitz on Cyprus would wreck the conference. It would never get off the ground.

'Why should Rassitz deal with you?' Fletcher asked. 'They have their own supply.'

'Rassitz wasn't aware he was dealing with us until I told him.'

'You told him?' Fletcher asked in surprise.

'Yes,' Veti said patiently. 'You see Pula was doing quite a lot of double dealing, so we decided to cut out the middle man and deal direct.'

'Was?' Fletcher asked.

'He won't any more,' Veti said. 'In fact he won't be practising any more.'

So Pula was dead, Fletcher thought. It didn't unduly surprise him. He had been a fool to play the Turks and the Communists, one against the other.

'And Rassitz was still prepared to do business with you?'

'Yes. It was too late for him to do an about-turn, and our goods are so tempting.'

'Just what are you supplying Rassitz with?' Fletcher asked seriously.

Veti remained silent, contemplating his answer.

'It is too late for you to stop Rassitz now,' he said finally, 'so I can tell you. He has a

161

shipment of short range guided missiles!'

Missiles! Fletcher thought. My God, no wonder there had been so much secrecy. With a battery of guided missiles Rassitz would be able to call the tune. But that wasn't all.

'He also has on board a number of technicians to supervise the siting arrangements.'

A pregnant silence followed his remark. Even the wild noises from behind the curtained door seemed to disappear. Fletcher's brain only registered the fact that Communist-supplied guided missiles and crews were being supplied to Rassitz for use on Cyprus. If they ever reached the island the present delicate equilibrium would become unbalanced. The island would erupt. But it could escalate into a major conflict, not only between Greece and Turkey, but between East and West. Now Fletcher realised why the Russians had passed on this information to Spencer. This was not of their doing. They saw the danger of creating another Cuba, even in miniature. But the Albanians, backed and pushed by the Chinese, were more adventurous – or reckless. As for Rassitz – he was only the vehicle for getting the missiles on to the island, and in his blind drunken lust for power he was prepared to deal with anybody.

Fletcher had most of the picture now. Pula, the middle man, offering a shipment of missiles to Rassitz. Dr Sleitser, alias Lofer, providing the cover for building up the stock pile and shipping them to Cyprus. But the weapons had to come from a Communist state, instead of the West. This was a private arrangement Pula had made. This was what Salunda and Kasim had suspected – that they were being supplied with Communist weapons and being made a tool for Communist intrigue. This was what Kasim had found out and that was why he had been murdered.

'What about the war heads?' Fletcher asked flatly.

'Conventional,' Veti replied. 'But they could be otherwise!'

At least that was some consolation, Fletcher thought. So far nothing nuclear had arrived on the island – so far!

A drunken reveller suddenly stumbled through the curtains. Veti gave a sharp order for him to be ejected. The man at the window turned and watched Fletcher whilst the drunk was quickly removed.

'What about Sleitser?' Fletcher asked, taking advantage of Veti's readiness to talk. 'Is he one of your men?'

Veti gave a deep chuckle as if he found the question amusing.

'For a man who has arrived at the critical place almost on the appointed hour you know very little,' he said.

'I travelled the short direct route,' Fletcher said, 'and fast!'

Veti looked impressed.

'Dr Sleitser was formerly Colonel Loferbraun of the German Army of Occupation, here in Greece. He was in command of coastal artillery. When he left Greece he was sent to work on the V bomb. So you see, Fettos, what a useful man he was to Pula. Not only did he know the right site for his archaeological camp, but he also had the necessary type of background to impress the Turks.'

Veti was being remarkably frank. He must be very confident of success, Fletcher thought.

'You haven't got all the answers,' Veti added quietly.

Fletcher looked at him, puzzled by his remark. What did he mean? What else was there for him to find out? Was he referring to Kasim's murder, or to the attempt on his life?

'Why don't you tell me then?' he asked.

Veti shook his head.

'No, Fettos, we'll leave that as a surprise for you!'

The man at the window called to Veti who went and joined him. Fletcher stood up to see what they were looking at, but was ordered to sit down again. Veti gave a grunt of satisfaction. Rassitz or some of his party had arrived! It was time for Fletcher to leave. Somehow he had to get out of their clutches and stop Rassitz getting on that boat. He glanced at the man with the gun. He had the hard look and the steady hand of a professional. It wasn't going to be easy, but it had to be done. Even Salunda was now secondary to stopping Rassitz.

Again the drunk staggered into the room, but his time he was accompanied by another equally intoxicated reveller. Fletcher's pulse quickened. Behind the mask of one of them was Mario! Fletcher recognised his clothing and the scar on his forearm. He braced himself and gripped the legs of the stool on which he was sitting.

Veti gave an impatient cry.

'Get them out!' he shrieked.

Again the man at the window covered Fletcher with his gun, as his friend struggled to eject the two drunks. One of them appeared to be on the verge of collapsing. He clung on to the man, his arms around his neck. Fletcher remained motionless, waiting for his opportunity. Veti brought out his own automatic and waved the man at the window to go to the other's assistance. Hurriedly the man crossed the room, his revolver still in his hand. When he reached the drunks, he raised his arm as if to strike one of them on the head. But Mario must have been waiting for the move and with all his weight he butted the man, sending him backwards on to the floor. Instantly Fletcher made his move. His stool flew across the room like a rocket and hit Veti in the chest. Veti gave an almost hysterical shriek as Fletcher lunged for the curtained opening. Fletcher felt a grab at his clothing, but he disentangled himself. He didn't like leaving Mario, but it had to be. At the doorway he flung himself bodily into the carnival crowd. Instead of making for the Syrian's house he headed towards the square. Veti would expect him to try to stop the Turks, but Fletcher had another idea. Ikarios! Unless he was mistaken, Ikarios was hunting the same thing as he was, and Ikarios had a naval frigate anchored off the bay. There wasn't time to harbour grievances, not with a boat load of guided missiles a few kilometres away, ready to sail for Cyprus.

The harbour front was even more congested than before and the crowd more intoxicated. Any second Fletcher expected to feel a bullet smack into his back. He knew Veti would not hesitate to fire now. He had abused their hospitality. It would be total war from now on. His only hope was to get to Ikarios before they caught up with him.

As he fought his way through the crowd he noticed the frigate was still in the same position that it had been before. He only hoped Ikarios was also.

Eventually he managed to force his way

166

into the foyer of the hotel where he had seen Ikarios on the balcony. It was deserted, except for a women sitting in a small office reading a newspaper as if the carnal exhibition of revelry which was going on around her was an everyday occurrence.

Fletcher dashed over to her.

'Inspector Ikarios,' he said. 'Where is he?'

She looked him up and down.

'Damn you,' Fletcher fumed. 'Where is he? It is important.'

'First floor room seven,' she said calmly, and leant forward and pressed a button on her desk. In the foyer a bell started ringing. Fletcher was half-way up the stairs before it stopped. As he reached the first-floor landing, the door to room seven opened and Sergeant Nepolis appeared, gun in hand. He smiled when he saw Fletcher. Not a pleasant, welcoming smile, but that of a man who was about to settle an old score.

'I want to see the Inspector,' Fletcher said, ignoring the man's menacing attitude. 'It is important.'

He brushed past the Sergeant and entered the bedroom. Ikarios, who was standing by the balcony door, gave a visible look of surprise. His eyes narrowed.

'You, Fettos,' he snarled.

'I have some information for you, Inspector,' Fletcher said quickly. 'Important information.'

The Inspector's face didn't relax.

'About what?' he snapped.

'Abdul Rassitz,' Fletcher said.

The Inspector and the Sergeant exchanged quick glances.

'What about him?' the Inspector asked. His tone was only slightly less aggressive.

'He is on the island,' Fletcher said, 'collecting a party of terrorists together to sail for Cyprus.'

The Inspector started to laugh.

'You must be mad,' he sneered. 'Besides, what do you know about Rassitz?'

Fletcher looked first at the Inspector and then at the Sergeant. They were both watching him. The Sergeant had his back to the door, and the gun was still in his hand. Fletcher tried again.

'I tell you it is true, Inspector. Rassitz and some of his men are on the island.'

'And how are they going to get off?' Ikarios asked.

'They are in league with Dr Sleitser, the archaeologist. He has a boat hidden in a cave near his camp.'

'Very good,' Ikarios said nodding his head, 'very good. Now we not only have a Turkish terrorist in our midst, but also a German gun-runner.'

He turned to his Sergeant.

'What do you make of this, Sergeant?' he asked. 'We come here looking for a murderer

168

and end up with an army of terrorists.'

'I would like to know how he got his information,' the Sergeant said acidly.

Ikarios came up closer to Fletcher.

'So would I,' he snarled. He flung his hand across Fletcher's face, but Fletcher had been expecting the move and parried the blow. He controlled his temper. What was the Inspector playing at? As a member of Greek Security he would know that Rassitz was in the area, and he had been very quick to look into Kronos' death. Why was he suddenly acting the innocent?

'I don't know what your game is, Inspector,' he fumed, 'but I am warning you that Rassitz is on the island and will be sailing for Cyprus. Use your head, man. Do you think I would come bursting in here unless I knew what I was saying?'

'How do you know all this, Fettos?' the Inspector asked, a mocking expression on his face. 'You are only a simple fisherman. Remember?'

He stormed over to the balcony and closed the louvred shutters. Fletcher was trapped with two armed sadistic policemen. He was in for a rough time. He cursed himself for having come to the hotel. He should have gone to the Syrian's house. The Inspector and the Sergeant stood looking at him. It was only a question of who intended to make the first move.

A knock at the bedroom door eased the tension. The Sergeant cast a quick glance at the Inspector and then went to the door. Fletcher watched closely. An automatic appeared in the Inspector's hand and Fletcher knew he wouldn't need much encouraging to make him use it.

The Sergeant opened the door and stood to one side as two men entered the rom. One of them was Andros Zonakas! But the other man was also familiar. He was the man who had been on the pier reading a newspaper when Fletcher and Mario had last visited the island! Their presence killed any lingering doubts Fletcher might have had of being able to persuade the Inspector to help him. He knew now what their game was; he wasn't going to need Veti to tell him.

Zonakas was surprised to see him. He slowly placed his hat on a nearby table and lit a cigarette.

'Well,' he said. 'This is indeed unexpected.'

'So you are at the back of this after all,' Fletcher sighed.

Zonakas smiled. A confident, conceited smile.

'I must confess I have taken more than a passing interest.'

'Why?' Fletcher asked. 'Are you trying to wreck the conference?'

'Oh! no Stefan. We want the conference to

170

proceed as planned. Only we want it to go our way.'

'And if Rassitz and his men get to Cyprus, you think that will help you?'

Zonakas pursed his mouth and raised his eyebrows questioningly.

'Will Rassitz get to Cyprus?' he asked.

'So that's your game,' Fletcher muttered. He recalled Veti's remarks about Pula. He had been a double agent working for the Communists and the Greeks, not working for the Turks, as Fletcher had thought! A flood of answers raced through his head. Salunda and Kasim's suspicions had not only been about the Communists, but also the Greeks. She had felt they were being used and she was correct. Zonakas had planted Pula and Dr Sleitser as bait to get Rassitz within their grasp. He had even used the Communists to help them. Fletcher couldn't help but admire his ingenuity. The promise of a boat load of missiles must have been very tempting to Rassitz. So tempting that he had taken the bait. But he would never get them to Cyprus. Zonakas intended to see to that. Zonakas and the naval frigate anchored off the harbour. When Rassitz left the island, he would be intercepted and exposed to the world as an aggressor and a Communist dupe. The Turks would be the warmongers, the trouble makers. The Greek would have scored a double victory. They

171

would have Rassitz safely behind bars, or six foot under the ground, and they would have strengthened their claim for 'enosis'.

But Zonakas' scheme had come adrift. Veti had found out that Pula had been playing the double agent. It wasn't a popular game to play, and he had paid the price. But Veti had also visited Rassitz! He had gone to protect the interests of his principals so perhaps there was another ace in the pack, of which Zonakas was not aware!

'Clever?' Zonakas asked like a schoolboy fishing for compliments.

'Very,' Fletcher agreed. 'But let me give you a warning. The Communists don't like to be monkeyed about. They become very annoyed.'

Zonakas wasn't worried.

'So long as Veti gets paid, he won't cry.'

'I wouldn't be too sure about that,' Fletcher said and added: 'Have you seen Pula during the past twenty-four hours?'

Zonakas looked up sharply.

'You have been busy,' he sneered.

'More than you think,' Fletcher retorted, 'and I would suggest your boys here drag themselves away from the carnival and do the same. You might find things aren't as you imagine. You might also find Pula's body!'

Zonakas' face clouded over and Ikarios gave an impatient snort.

'If he knows something we'll get it out of

172

him,' Ikarios said angrily.

Zonakas relaxed again.

'Stefan, I think you are playing with us,' he said lightly. 'You British like your sport.'

The Inspector snorted and made an unpleasant remark.

'I do wish you wouldn't get so emotional, Inspector,' Zonakas sighed. He looked at Fletcher. 'Take him away,' he snapped. 'He is beginning to bore me.' He turned his back on Fletcher and walked over to the balcony doors.

It was the signal the Sergeant and his colleague had been waiting for.

'We'll meet again, Zonakas,' Fletcher said, before he was grabbed.

'Perhaps,' Zonakas replied, but Fletcher didn't hear him. He was being bundled out of the room. At the head of the stairs he struggled to get out of their grasp. The thoughts of being pummelled with a truncheon gave him extra strength. He felt one of his arms come free and he swung round to lash out at his other capturer, but before he even connected, a crashing blow to his head sent him reeling down the stairs.

CHAPTER NINE

The movement of the truck brought Fletcher back to consciousness. He was lying on the floor, his hands tied behind his back and his mouth gagged. His head throbbed and ached. Each time the vehicle went over an uneven section of track, the vibrations sent a wave of shooting pains through his body. He moved his feet and felt someone lying beside him. He heard the mumble of voices around him – German voices! He tried to think clearly. The last thing he could remember was talking to Ikarios and Zonakas. He had been bundled out of the room and then the blow to his head. But they had not taken him to the police station! Why hadn't they done that? Was it because of Zonakas? Would he have been too much of an embarrassment for him? Again he heard German voices. He was being taken to Sleitser's camp! Zonakas was going to let Sleitser dispose of him. It would solve all his problems. His role in the plot would never come to light.

Fletcher moved his position and saw Mario lying beside him. He was also bound and gagged. Fletcher wondered who had delivered him into the hands of Sleitser. Veti or Ikarios?

The truck bounced its way along a particularly rough section of track and stopped. The other occupants scrambled over the two gagged bodies and jumped to the ground. One of them was ordered to stand guard and the rest shuffled away.

Fletcher tried to free his hands, but they were securely bound. He slowly moved his body until he could see out of the open end of the truck. The sky was still being stabbed with rays of bright lights from the town, and a cavalcade of rockets spluttered into a shower of golden stars.

They were at Sleitser's camp, as he had thought. He could see the silhouetted shape of the temple foundations.

Footsteps came up to the truck, and a muffled conversation was held with their guard.

A flashlight shone in their faces and they were roughly dragged off the vehicle.

'Up!' a voice barked in German. 'Up!'

Fletcher was lifted on to his feet. So was Mario. They exchanged quick glances. Mario, like Fletcher, looked as if he had been brutally overpowered, but his flashing eyes were still full of fight.

The man who was giving the orders was the heavily built German, whom Fletcher had seen with the truck in the town.

They were standing outside the canopy

which backed against the vertical face of the amphitheatre. It was the entrance to a cave. At the end of the opening, a series of dimly lit electric light bulbs ran into the side of the rock face.

A vicious blow from the German's boot sent Mario stumbling into the passageway. The other man was less sadistic and Fletcher was pushed under the canopy.

A single line railway-track ran into the cave. It was rusted and obviously unused. At the head of the cave they were pushed into a steep tunnel which ran off at a right angle. Fletcher leant against the sides to stop himself from stumbling over the smoothened rock face which formed the floor. On the sides of the tunnel were a number of carvings – relics from the days when the Germans had used it during the occupation of Greece.

It was an uncomfortable and dangerous descent, made even more unpleasant by the goading and jabs from the heavily built German, whose delight would have been complete if Fletcher and Mario had both gone reeling to the bottom of the tunnel.

Gradually the descent became less severe and the tunnel broadened out into a large, subterranean cavern. It was well lit and at the open end Fletcher could see the white stern of a boat. The cavern pulsated an atmosphere of activity which was made vocal by a throbbing generator.

177

They were taken to a room formed in the side of the cavern. A small, dark, dimly lit cave. Fletcher sat on the ground beside Mario and one of the Germans stood guard at the entrance. Again Fletcher struggled with his bonds, but the nylon cord cut into his wrists each time he made a movement with his hands. The gag was equally uncomfortable. It pulled at the sides of his cheeks and the cotton waste which had been stuffed in his mouth had a choking effect. It took all his concentration to breathe evenly and stay alive.

Presently the sadistic German returned with Dr Sleitser. The Doctor was much smaller than the two guards, but his face had the sharp, hard features, of a man used to giving orders. His grey hair and matching beard, however, gave an academic air to his otherwise military features. He stood with his hands behind his back, silently looking at Fletcher and Mario. There was no cruelty in his small pebble-like eyes – only annoyance. He walked over to Fletcher and looked down at him.

'When you were brought to me by our Turkish friends,' he said in a broken Greek accent, 'I thought I had seen you before.' He paused. 'Now I know where that was.'

His face hardened. He turned to his assistant.

'Take off his gag,' he snapped in German.

178

The German pulled the gag away from Fletcher's mouth and took out the cotton waste. Fletcher thankfully swallowed and stretched his mouth.

Sleitser leant over him again.

'What does Spencer know of this?' he asked.

Fletcher looked at him.

'Who is Spencer?' he asked slowly.

The German's face flushed. The man standing beside him swung a vicious blow with his foot which sank into the pit of Fletcher's stomach. For a while Fletcher lay fighting for breath, but even as he was regaining control of his body his brain was furiously deciding what action to take. If the Greeks hadn't told Sleitser who he was working for, then he didn't intend to help him out. It wasn't something that was shouted from the rooftops. He still had sufficient faith to believe he would get out of the Doctor's clutches alive, and the fewer people who were aware of his work the better.

'Who is Spencer?' he gasped.

'You know who he is,' Sleitser yelled. 'I saw you sitting near him at the Acropolis when I was there with Professor Kay.'

Fletcher was still struggling for breath.

'Acropolis!' he stammered, 'I have not been there for a long time.'

'You deny you are working for the British?' the Doctor fumed.

'I work for Mattu,' Fletcher said.

'So you have told me,' the Doctor said slowly. 'Then tell me why Inspector Ikarios should want me to get rid of you. If you are one of Mattu's men, I would have thought the Inspector would have been only too pleased to have taken you back to Athens.'

'The Inspector is flying bigger kites than Mattu,' Fletcher said evenly.

'But he is still a policeman,' the Doctor retorted, 'and they do not hand over one of their prisoners unless they have a very good reason. But enough of this.'

He motioned the man beside him to refix the gag. When he had accomplished the task, Fletcher found himself in an even more choking position than he had been before.

'Let me just tell you what is going to happen to you both,' Sleitser said. There was a faint smile on his lips.

'When we are out at sea,' he added, 'you will both be shot and then thrown overboard!'

He turned and walked to the exit, where he hesitated. 'If you are more forthcoming with your answers, next time we talk,' he said slowly, 'it would be to your advantage.'

Like hell! Fletcher thought. Answers or no answers, the end would just be the same. The outlook was pretty bleak, but not without hope. He couldn't see Rassitz going blindly into a trap, not after having been warned by Veti, and Fletcher had also been in the game too long to fight all his battles single-handed. By now his friend, the Patriarch, would have put Spencer in the picture, and the ball would be in his court.

The heavily built German made a menacing gesture and ordered them to stand up. Fletcher and Mario had no alternative but to obey him. They struggled to their feet and allowed themselves to be pushed out of the room, and along the cavern to where Sleitser's boat nestled between two vertical faces of the cliff. Fletcher liked the look of the boat. It was a motor yacht, about a hundred and twenty feet long, which could have graced the harbour of any fashionable resort. A single blue funnel rose from its gleaming white superstructure, and white canvas awnings were stretched over its deck and fastened to glistening brass posts. It was brilliantly lit from stern to stern, giving the impression of a luxury boat with a full complement of pleasure-seeking guests.

The inlet also held Fletcher's attention. Around three sides ran a narrow wooden platform. The roof was a steel-framed structure, whilst seawards was a large camouflaged curtain which explained why he had not seen it when they had sailed past. It would also be hidden from above, he thought. The heavy steel beams which spanned the two vertical faces of the rocks had not been put there to carry the steel sheeting alone. On top of them would be earth and grass camouflaging. It was a cleverly formed hideaway for an E-boat waiting to pounce on unsuspecting shipping – or for Sleitser's yacht to prepare to sail to Cyprus!

Fletcher followed Mario along the footwalk towards the gang-plank. As they passed in line with one of the saloons, he saw a number of heads – dark sleek heads – Turkish heads! He felt disappointed. Although he hadn't seen Rassitz or Salunda, he had a feeling they would be aboard. He didn't mind Rassitz walking into Ikarios's trap, but he felt different about Salunda. Ikarios wouldn't show any mercy. He cursed the man, and hoped that Spencer had returned from his trip to Rhodes earlier than had been expected.

They were taken to a small cabin at the stern of the boat, near the engine room. When the door was locked behind them, the only light they got came from the narrow opening between the deck and the bottom of the door.

Fortunately, however, their feet had not been bound and they could move about. The cabin was about seven feet by nine, with the bulkhead sloping with the stern of the boat, but it was hot and unventilated.

Mario nudged Fletcher and by a series of

grunts indicated that he wanted to pull off Fletcher's gag with his fingers. Fletcher bent down and Mario got the tips of his fingers into the gag. After a number of abortive attempts it came away from Fletcher's mouth. He spat out the cotton waste and did the same for Mario.

'What happened?' Fletcher asked.

'The place was swarming with police,' Mario spat. 'I got clear of Veti, but before I could get to the Syrian's house two of the local police jumped me. The next thing I knew I was on the truck with you.'

'Ikarios was responsible for my presence also. Zonakas and Ikarios are the master-minds of the whole thing. Sleitser is working for them. So was Pula before Veti killed him.'

'Why should Zonakas and Ikarios want to supply Rassitz with weapons?' Mario asked in surprise.

'They don't,' Fletcher said, 'but they want him to be caught with them in his possession. That is why that frigate is anchored off the bay. As soon as Sleitser gets into the open sea the frigate will close in.'

'I am surprised that Rassitz has fallen into the trap.'

'So am I. Originally Rassitz thought Sleitser was supplying the weapons from Germany. When Veti found out that Pula was in league with Ikarios they dispensed with his services, and dealt direct with Rassitz. So he must know where the weapons are coming from.'

'If Rassitz knows what is going on, why didn't he pull out?'

'Two reasons,' Fletcher said. 'First of all we don't know exactly what Veti told him. They are looking after their own interests and that means trouble of any kind, and secondly, Rassitz is prepared to risk anything to get that cargo to Cyprus.'

'What is the cargo?' Mario asked.

'Guided missiles,' Fletcher said. 'A battery of them, together with a crew of technicians to show Rassitz' men the know-how.'

Mario gave an appreciative whistle.

'They will be short range rockets which can be directed on to any target,' Fletcher went on to explain, 'If Rassitz can get them sited in the right places in the Troodos Mountains, he can direct a rain of terror on to any part of the island. And Veti has promised him a further stockpile. Can you imagine what a strong position it would put the Turks in?'

'Sure,' Mario agreed, 'and that bastard Rassitz would just love it. We should have killed him as I said.'

'Don't give up hope,' Fletcher said. 'I lit a candle before we left Piraeus.'

Even in the darkness Fletcher could see Mario's teeth flash into a smile.

'I have a lot of faith in your candles,'

Mario said, 'but what if Ikarios and Rassitz have also lit candles?'

Before Fletcher had time to answer the ship's engine thudded into action. The cabin shook as the pistons started to pulsate. Fletcher tried to yell above the crescendo, but his voice was drowned. He gave up and instead searched the cabin and the door for a sharp edge to sever his bonds. But it was in vain. He tried the full weight of his body against the door, but it was like pushing against a steel barrier. Even when Mario joined him they still made no impression.

They felt the motion of the ship as it cut through the inshore swell and knew they were under way. The noise from the engine combined with the heat was becoming almost unbearable. The perspiration rolled down their faces and their eardrums were becoming punch drunk.

Fletcher sat on the deck and buried his head between his knees. In an endeavour to distract his thoughts from their mental torture, he thought of Zonakas and marvelled at the man's cunning and ingenuity. He wondered how long it had taken him to conjure up the whole plot. Weeks? Months? Long before the Rhodes Conference had been initiated, that was certain. Then why hadn't the Greek Government called off the plot? It would have been an act of faith. It said little for their case for 'enosis' when they had to engage their unofficial agent to provoke sympathy for their cause. He managed a smile as he wondered what Zonakas' true feelings had been when he had questioned him about the possibility of a coup upsetting the conference. Despite his outward display of calm, it must have caused him a certain amount of irritation and anxiety.

Fletcher had sat in his pose for about twenty minutes when the engines suddenly stopped. The silence was pregnant. Mario gave an audible sigh of relief. Fletcher struggled to his feet and again searched the cabin for a means of severing their bonds.

'We must get rid of these bonds,' he whispered.

'I have searched,' Mario said. 'There is nothing. Where do you think we are?'

A faint muffled plop from a rocket gave them the answer. They were in the harbour at Serifos.

'The carnival is in its final fling,' Fletcher said. 'That means we'll be going to sea soon.'

He stopped his search.

'Mario, you heard Sleitser,' he said. 'When they come for us we must play for time, even if it means talking. Tell them anything. Every second is vital.'

'Anything you say, Stefan, but if I can get my hands free it won't be talking alone, I assure you.'

'Wait for the right moment,' Fletcher warned. 'There are too many of them.'

He sat down again and leant against the bulkhead. The next few hours were going to be critical – very critical.

Presently the engines shuddered into action again and their mental torture repeated itself. But added to their anguish was the uncertainty of knowing when Sleitser was going to deal with them. Fletcher didn't doubt his intentions. The last thing Zonakas or Ikarios would want was Fletcher or Mario returning to Piraeus alive. In fact the Inspector had already tried to kill him. It had been the Inspector and Zonakas who had hired the killer to knife him in his bed. Fletcher had become too meddlesome. When he had been seen on the island it had made them act. His link with Kronos and his visit to the island had been too much for them, but the Inspector had no grounds for bringing him in for questioning, so they had tried to get rid of him altogether. When they saw the attempt had failed they killed their hired assassin before he could talk. The Inspector had then trumped up the telephone call from a neighbour to make sure they searched his apartment. They knew well enough that there would be blood about. But they hadn't bargained on Kasim's body being there. That had taken them by surprise as much as it had Fletcher.

Fletcher also realised why Salunda had engaged him to take her to the island, and why she had sent him into Serifos. It hadn't been to kill time while she visited Rassitz. It had been to make sure he was seen by Ikarios' watch dog! When she had said that she and Kasim suspected they were being used, she had not meant by the Communists, as he had thought, but the Greeks themselves! She had used Fletcher as bait. She had warned him against returning to Piraeus because she knew Ikarios would be after him. But if she suspected so much, then why had she let Rassitz and his men come aboard the boat? What were they up to?

At a time when dawn would be breaking, Fletcher got the first hint of an answer to his questions. Above the engine noise he heard a faint 'crack'. Instantly he became alert. Mario nudged him – he had also heard it. Fletcher shuffled to the door and lay on the floor, his ear to the opening. Again there was a 'crack' and another, and another. It was revolver shooting! A short burst from a sub machine gun confirmed that a battle was taking place. He shuffled back to Mario and shouted: 'Revolvers!' in his ear.

He counted a further three bursts from the machine gun and seven revolver cracks, before all went silent. Even the engines came to a stand still.

'A boarding party?' Mario asked excitedly.

'Too much to hope for,' Fletcher said. 'I think Rassitz has tried to take over.'

'I hope he has succeeded,' Mario said, 'but I wouldn't trust him to let us go free.'

'No, Mario, I agree. If Rassitz is in charge we are no better off, except perhaps we may have more time to play with.'

Footsteps came hurrying along the passageway. Quickly Fletcher went to the door and banged on it with his foot. Mario joined him, but nothing happened.

'I wonder where we are?' Fletcher asked.

'A long way from Cyprus,' Mario muttered. 'Could he be hiding off one of the islands during the day.'

'What about that frigate?' Fletcher asked. 'It hadn't been part of their plan to get anywhere near Cyprus. It must be dawn by now. Why hasn't that frigate closed in?'

Again someone approached. Before they had time to get to the door, the lock was turned. The light shone into the room, momentarily blinding them. Fletcher staggered into the corridor, Mario behind him.

It was a Turk who had opened the door. A small man who looked completely out of place in his monk's robes with a revolver in his hand.

'We heard the shots,' Fletcher said. 'What happened?'

The Turk gave a broad smile.

'It was time for us to take over from Sleitser,' he beamed. 'You are to come with me to our leader.'

'Cut these cords,' Fletcher said. 'We have been like this for hours.'

The Turk shook his head.

'No,' he said without remorse. 'That is for our leader to decide.'

Mario swore. Fletcher said nothing, but wondered what Rassitz was up to.

They followed the Turk along the narrow corridor and on to the deck. Two still forms lay in the shade. It was daylight, the sea was calm and the grey sky was receding behind an orange blanket.

As they passed the aft saloon, Fletcher saw Sleitser and some of his men looking grim and sullen. The Doctor was holding a blood-stained arm. On deck the Turks moved about with a confident air. Some of them wore the monk's robes whilst others were in various forms of carnival dress.

Rassitz was on the bridge. So was Salunda. With them was Ahmad and Rassitz' first lieutenant, the Turk Fletcher had seen at the villa. Salunda was staring straight ahead of her. Her face looked pale and drawn. A cardigan hung loosely over her shoulders. She was surprised to see them; it reflected in her face. Instinctively she moved towards Fletcher, but Rassitz stopped her.

'Stefan!' she exclaimed.

Rassitz stepped in front of her, his dark eyes giving no indication how he felt.

'Take them to the forward saloon,' he said flatly.

'These bonds?' Fletcher asked. 'Are they necessary?'

Rassitz didn't answer and turned his back on them. As they left the bridge Fletcher caught a glimpse of Salunda's face. She looked worried.

'I don't think he is going to prove very friendly,' Mario muttered when they were in the saloon.

'We are about to find out,' Fletcher whispered, as Rassitz and his first lieutenant appeared at the doorway. Rassitz stood in the entrance, his hard face looking even more ruthless and determined than his photograph had indicated.

'You have become very involved in my affairs,' he said in Greek without any trace of accent, but in a flat, dour tone.

'Too much for my liking,' Fletcher replied seriously.

'What were you doing in Serifos?'

Fletcher had anticipated the question.

'Looking for Salunda,' he replied.

'What are you?' Rassitz asked sharply. 'A romantic or a fool?'

Fletcher shrugged.

'A bit of both, perhaps.'

Rassitz gave him a contemptuous scowl,

191

but Fletcher could take his derision.

'And if you had found her?' Rassitz asked.

'I intended to warn her,' Fletcher said.

'About what?'

'That the cargo you were being supplied with came from the Communists and that Inspector Ikarios knew all about it.'

The Turk's eyes narrowed.

'How do you know this?' he snapped.

'Look, Rassitz, I am no fool. I have been in this game as long as you. I have even supplied your people with guns. I knew what you were after. Kronos told me. When Salunda took me to Serifos and I came across Dr Sleitser, I put two and two together.'

'You still haven't answered my question,' Rassitz said.

'When I was in Serifos I recognised one of the Inspector's men on the pier. Later the same evening a hired assassin tried to kill me. I figured it was either one of your men or one of the Inspector's, so I went to your villa to get the answer from Salunda. When I was there I saw you talking to Veti. I know Veti and who he works for. He is a Communist, Rassitz, or didn't you know?'

Rassitz didn't answer.

'I have a lot of contacts,' Fletcher continued, 'so I made it my business to find out what was going on.'

He let Rassitz fill in the gaps himself.

'But you are a Greek,' Rassitz said

pointedly. 'Why should you want to prevent your own countrymen from capturing me and my men.'

It was a good question and Fletcher knew he would never convince the man that he wanted to help him.

'I wasn't worried about you or your men,' he said. 'I only wanted to help her.'

'But she is one of us,' Rassitz snapped.

'No, Rassitz, she is not,' Fletcher replied evenly, 'nor was her brother Kasim. She spent a night and a day on my boat. You learn a lot about people on a boat. She is not one of your followers, Rassitz.'

There was a short, electric silence before Rassitz spoke.

'You speak dangerous words,' he said.

Fletcher was aware of this, but having gone so far he intended to go the full limit. If Spencer had got his message, then he was overdue. If he hadn't, then it wouldn't make any difference to the outcome. Rassitz would never let them off the boat alive.

'Why should I lie to you?' he asked. 'You will kill us no matter what I say.'

'Very true,' Rassitz said flatly. 'It is unfortunate, but it is true.'

He came further into the saloon followed by his two henchmen.

'You puzzle me, though,' he confessed. 'I still can't understand your actions.'

'Perhaps there are still some of us who do

not want war to break out again on Cyprus,' Fletcher remarked.

Rassitz' face darkened.

'Don't lie to me or I will kill you now,' he yelled. 'You are a gun-runner. You make money out of wars.'

'But not with your type of weapons.'

'Bah!' Rassitz cried. 'You are a fool after all. Does it make any difference whether you kill a man with a rifle or a rocket.'

'Perhaps it does to some people,' Fletcher said goading the man. 'To Kasim for instance?'

'Kasim was an idealist,' Rassitz fumed. 'He was weak and scared. The very mention of the word Communist was enough to make him run.'

'So you killed him?'

'He killed himself. He disobeyed my orders. No one does that and lives. The moment he put his foot on Serifos he had signed his own death warrant.

'And you put his body in my apartment?' Fletcher asked.

'Yes,' Rassitz agreed. 'In your apartment.'

'Why?' Fletcher asked.

'To make sure it would be discovered, and to get you out of the way!'

It was Fletcher's turn to be surprised.

'So you telephoned Ikarios,' Fletcher said.

'Yes, we telephoned the Inspector. We thought he would appreciate the gesture, especially after his attempt to kill you had failed.'

The Turk's remark made Fletcher realise he knew more than Fletcher had credited him with. His next remark confirmed this suspicion.

'The British are our allies,' Rassitz said slowly. 'We didn't want to kill two of their best men ourselves.' He shrugged. 'But if the Greeks were prepared to do it, why not help them?'

For the first time Rassitz smiled, showing a row of uneven stained teeth.

'But you are prepared to do it now,' Fletcher said.

'Yes,' Rassitz said sadly. 'Now there is no alternative.'

The gloves were off. There was no point in trying to fool Rassitz any longer. He had been playing with Fletcher like a cat with a mouse.

'How long have you known?' he said.

'From the moment you started looking for Lofer. No one does that unless they want to commit suicide.' He paused dramatically. 'Or unless they are British.' His remark made him laugh. 'That's why we engaged you to visit Serifos. We wanted to watch developments. Kill two birds with one stone. You see we also suspected the Greeks of having a hand in this.'

Mario swore under his breath. He didn't

like being used as a decoy by anyone – least of all Rassitz.

'And as you have already explained,' Rassitz continued, 'one of the Inspector's men recognised you and naturally they didn't want a British agent interfering in their little scheme, so they tried to kill you.'

'You appear to have thought of everything,' Fletcher said.

'Of course we have,' Rassitz snapped. 'Do you think I would risk putting a foot on Greek territory without taking precautions.'

'What about their frigate?' Fletcher asked.

'Look out of that window,' Rassitz said, 'and tell me what you see.'

Fletcher did as Rassitz had said. On the horizon was a naval vessel.

'That is their frigate,' Rassitz explained. 'Now look out of the opposite window.'

Even before he looked Fletcher knew what he would see. Another naval vessel!

'That is ours,' Rassitz said with glee.

But Fletcher had seen something Rassitz hadn't. There were two vessels on the horizon!

'If the Greek makes one move, our destroyer will open up on him,' Rassitz went on. 'We played them at their own game and have beaten them. They are like novices.'

Rassitz was getting warmed up. His eyes were flashing around the room as if he were looking for a disbeliever amongst his group of disciples.

Fletcher's excitement was also mounting. Could that other vessel on the distant horizon be the answer to his message to Spencer? It was overdue. Dawn had been the proposed time. And if it was? He had to play for time. Keep Rassitz talking.

'I admire your thoroughness, Rassitz,' he said slowly, 'but I must admit you surprised me by having dealings with the Communists.'

'Bah!' Rassitz snarled. 'Communist, capitalist, what does it matter so long as you get the weapons. Did the U.N. throw up their arms in disgust when the Greek Cypriots got their supply from Czechoslovakia? They have been dealing with the Communists from the very beginning. You British are an odd race. When it suits your own purpose you turn a blind eye like your great Nelson, but if it doesn't, you make a lot of noise about it.'

'What about the technicians?' Fletcher persisted. 'You must admit that is inviting criticism.'

'I have my sites already prepared. It will take me two days to install the equipment and perhaps a further two or three days to pass on the necessary instructions. Don't forget some of my men have been trained on similar equipment in Turkey. It will not take them long to become adjusted.'

'A week,' Fletcher muttered. 'Long enough

for the Greeks to make capital out of it.'

'They won't say a word,' Rassitz quickly replied. 'Not a word. How do you think it would sound if they announced that I, Abdul Rassitz, had gone to a Greek island with my men, boarded a boat equipped with missiles and sailed for Cyprus? Never mind the technicians; they are a mere detail. There are ten times the number of Communists working for the Greeks. The Greeks won't say a word or they will become the laughing stock of the world.'

He gave a deep, raucous laugh. The two Turks standing by the door joined him, but Fletcher doubted whether they had fully understood what Rassitz had been saying. His accent was becoming more difficult to follow, his speech more inarticulate. Fletcher watched him enjoy his moment. He looked like a wild man with his long hair straggling down the sides of his face. But despite his bedraggled appearance and his high-pitched screaming voice, there was something fiendishly magnetic about him. He had the satanic appeal of a devil's disciple.

Rassitz quietened down.

'Kasim spoke your words' he said, 'and so did many others. They even questioned my ability to go into the Greek stronghold and steal their treasure, but now they will eat their words. When these guns are in position that long bearded dupe of the Greek Government will have to recognise my presence.'

His face hardened and his eyes became glazed.

'For too long my people have been the underdog just because they were weak in numbers. Enosis! Enosis! Enosis!' He screamed the words. 'That's all we hear from them. Well, we don't want enosis. We want our people to live on the island as they wish, and not to become the lackeys of the men in Athens. If they want enosis then there must be a partition on the island. So you see why my guns are important.'

Fletcher understood him all right, but Rassitz, like a lot of men of his type, underestimated his opposition. A pistol pointing at the heart only gets results so long as it remains pointing that way, but it is impossible to keep the vigil up for ever.

'You could achieve the same results by peaceful means,' Fletcher said calmly.

'Talk! Talk!' Rassitz screamed. 'We have talked enough. Whenever we talk with them they produce a picture of Grivas and say no more. Now we will match their hero.'

'And the Rhodes Conference?' Fletcher asked.

'I know nothing about that,' Rassitz said. 'I have heard talk of it, that is all, but if such a conference takes place we will be talking

199

from strength, not weakness.'

The sudden appearance of an anxious-looking Turk at the doorway put paid to any further discussions.

'There is another boat!' the Turk said breathlessly.

Fletcher's pulse quickened. He cast a quick glance at Mario who had been standing listening to the discussion with a long scowling face. Mario nodded his head; he understood what was happening.

Rassitz stormed out of the saloon followed by his second-in-command. The other Turk remained on guard, the revolver still in his hand.

'We might have to swim for it,' Fletcher whispered. 'I don't think Rassitz will be very pleased to see the Royal Navy.'

'That guard,' Mario hissed. 'If only we could get the bonds free.'

A loud piercing whine made them freeze. Time seemed to stand still as a shell passed over the boat. A few seconds later there was a loud, muffled explosion.

'My God!' Fletcher exclaimed. 'They mean business.'

The boat sharply changed course, flinging Fletcher and Mario across the saloon. Fletcher cast a quick glance their guard who was hanging on to the handrail! Another Turk appeared at the doorway. It was Ahmad.

'The leader wants you on deck,' he said to the guard. He brought out his own revolver. 'I'll take over here.'

The guard didn't need any second bidding. He quickly disappeared.

Ahmad came into the saloon and stood looking at Fletcher and Mario. Fletcher held his breath. Which way was he going to jump?

'Your navy has arrived,' he said with a smile. He produced a dagger and stuck it forcibly into the table. 'You are well advised to leave this ship,' he said, and quickly left the saloon.

Another shell shrilled towards them making them lie flat on the deck. As soon as it passed over, Mario quickly cut his bonds, and then Fletcher's.

Again the boat suddenly changed course as it tried to weave its way out of the gun boat's range. At the same instant, Salunda staggered into the saloon. Quickly Fletcher grabbed her to stop her from crashing into the bulkhead. He put his arms around her and held her tight.

'You must go,' she said. 'He will kill you.'

'Come with us,' Fletcher pleaded, as he hung on to a small fixed table.

She tried to push him away.

'Please go,' she cried.

Again there was a wailing screech and another explosion. This time the explosion was perilously close. They were getting the range.

'You must come,' Fletcher yelled. 'If one of those shells hits this boat, it will go up like gunpowder.'

He ignored her resistance and pulled her off the floor. But he got no further. Standing in the entrance to the saloon, gun in hand, was Rassitz! He looked insane! His lips trembled with rage and his eyes protruded like two fiery balls. Even before he spoke he fired his revolver.

'British pig!' he screamed as the bullet went wild.

There was a tinkle of broken glass as Fletcher flung Salunda and himself behind a settee.

Crack! Crack! Two further shots ran out. But Rassitz was blind with rage, he was firing well of target.

'British pig,' he yelled again. 'I'll…'

He got no further. There was a gentle thump as Mario's knife found its home in Rassitz' chest! Rassitz gave a guttural groan and slumped to the floor.

Fletcher got to his feet and crossed over to the body. The dagger had sunk itself into Rassitz' heart. He would cause no more trouble. Mario withdrew the knife from the body, unconcerned, and wiped it on Rassitz' clothes.

Salunda had her head turned away, her face

in her hands. Fletcher went over to her and gently put his arms around her shoulders.

'Please go,' she cried. There were tears in her eyes.

The engine stopped and Ahmad ran into the saloon. He cast a quick glance at Rassitz' body and came over to Salunda.

'Kumel has stopped the boat. He is going to sink it before the British get here. We are to lower the lifeboats and make for our destroyer.'

Salunda regained her composure.

'It is as well,' she said.

Ahmad looked at Fletcher.

'For the sake of Allah,' he said, 'get off this boat before they discover the body.'

Fletcher turned to Salunda.

'Go,' she said, and managed a faint smile. 'I shall be all right with Ahmad.'

'Shall I see you again?' he asked.

'Oh! Yes,' she cried. 'Please go.'

'Quick,' Mario hissed impatiently.

As they ran out of the saloon, two Turks appeared. There was a look of surprise on their faces which Fletcher and Mario took advantage of. Before they knew what was happening Fletcher and Mario had waded into them. With a flurry of blows they were quickly pushed to one side. On the deck Fletcher hesitated only long enough to see in which direction the British ship lay, before flinging himself headlong into the sea. But even as they swam away, a spurt of machine-gun fire followed them from the bridge. The Turks didn't give up their prisoners without a fight!

CHAPTER TEN

'Nice boat,' Spencer remarked casually. 'Pity we didn't get it intact.'

He was standing on the deck of the destroyer, Fletcher at his side, watching the yacht sink into the sea. Mario was in the sick bay getting the scars of his battle with Veti and the police attended to.

'You could have done,' Fletcher pointed out, 'if you hadn't hung back for so damned long.'

'I agree,' Spencer said, 'but when I saw you swimming towards us I didn't want to spoil your pleasure. Besides, it solves a lot of problems this way. Less embarrassing all round.'

Fletcher watched the small boats make their way towards the two other naval vessels which had closed in on the sinking ship. The Turks were heading towards their own destroyer, whilst Sleitser and the remainder of the crew were rowing towards the Greek vessel. Through a pair of binoculars he could see Salunda in one of the Turkish boats.

'What happens now?' he asked.

'Nothing,' Spencer said lightly. 'Absolutely nothing. The incident is closed, but I think our Government will have a very successful conference. I suspect both the Turks and the Greeks will be more willing to co-operate.'

'No fuss, no publicity,' Fletcher muttered. 'Another incident nipped in the bud.'

'That about sums it up,' Spencer agreed.

The yacht gave a final shudder and went over on one side.

'All that expensive equipment,' Fletcher said sadly.

'Yes,' Spencer agreed, 'but it wouldn't surprise me if some of our naval boys came and did a bit of salvage work. The war office is rather keen to have a look at some of that stuff.'

He gave Fletcher a knowing look.

'Thank goodness for that,' Fletcher said brightly. 'I wouldn't like to think of Sleitser's work in hiding the boat and collecting the equipment together, being entirely wasted.'

'Oh! Don't worry yourself about Dr Sleitser, Fletcher. He is the only one who has enjoyed himself. As for the boat...' Spencer shrugged. 'Well, it was anchored off Trieste a week ago. It then went to Portoros for a day, then to Dubrovnik, and finally to Serifos. Of course on the way it called at Durres to pick up the stores.

Fletcher looked at him with surprise. Spencer was hiding his amusement behind a handkerchief as he mopped his brow.

'Well!' Fletcher exclaimed. 'How the devil...?'

'Oh, a friend in the Yugoslav Embassy gave me the tip off.'

'And Sleitser has actually been carrying out his archaeological workings.'

'Yes, so I am told. It appears he became very interested in the subject when he was here with the German army. When he was captured by the Russians at Peenemunde he studied it in earnest. After his release he continued his studies at Bonn University. A year ago he applied for permission to bring a small expedition to Delos to search along the Sacred Way for temple remains. However, when his background came to light I can only presume he was offered Serifos instead, on the understanding that he co-operated. No doubt the finances of his expedition were met by the Greek Government. So all things considered I think Dr Sleitser has little to complain about.'

'And I thought the coaster was bringing in the weapons,' Fletcher mused.

'That's probably what they wanted the Turks to believe, although I can hardly imagine them being that susceptible. Actually, I am told that Dr Sleitser shipped out quite a number of useful mosaics and marble statues, so no doubt they went via the coaster.'

'You say you don't think the Turks would

have been quite so susceptible,' Fletcher said, 'but surely they must have been. Obviously they suspected trickery, but if they knew about the yacht, why the devil go ahead at all?'

Spencer smiled.

'Do you see those two naval vessels over there?' he asked. 'One is Greek, the other is Turkish. They are about two hundred yards apart. Now it wouldn't surprise me if at this very minute each of them is trying to put a limpet mine on the hull of the other. It is as bad as that. They don't really want to kill each other so much as to put one over on the other.' He sighed. 'As for our little incident – well it is a form of Russian roulette. They point the gun, pull the trigger and if all is well they chalk one up to themselves. The Turks knew the Greeks wouldn't allow Rassitz to get away with a boat load of missiles from under their very noses, but they thought they could outsmart them. And they did! Don't forget, if it hadn't been for you and Mario, Rassitz would be well on his way to Cyprus.'

'I am surprised the Turkish Government are prepared to take such risks,' Fletcher said.

'Oh! They don't,' Spencer replied. 'They are very clever. Two days after Rassitz left Turkey his Government disowned him. They publicly denounced him. They even had the nerve to call in the Greek Ambassador and warn him that Rassitz would probably be stirring up trouble.'

'So if he failed in his bid they would have no case to answer,' Fletcher said.

'Precisely,' Spencer agreed. 'Even if he succeeded they would still disown him, but he would have produced a *fait accompli*. Whether the Turkish Government recognised him or not, he still had to be reckoned with.'

'So they couldn't lose?' Fletcher asked.

'No,' Spencer said. 'They couldn't.'

'Well, at least it is good strategy.'

'Very good.'

'What about the Greeks? Were they in the same position?'

'A very similar one,' Spencer said thoughtfully, 'but slightly more vulnerable. Zonakas, as you know, acts in an unofficial capacity for them. He thinks up their grandiose schemes and if they succeed the government adopts them as their own. If they fail they just deny his existence. He has no official capacity.'

'But they had more to lose than the Turks,' Fletcher persisted.

'Yes, I agree, but under their very noses.' Spencer put up his hands in disgust. 'They were entitled to think they could get away with it. My God! There must be some red faces about.'

'What will happen to Zonakas and Ikarios

now?' Fletcher asked.

'Ikarios will be spending the rest of his service days on Crete. He will not be seen again on the mainland, I can assure you. As for Zonakas. Well, he will have performed his last unofficial service for his Government. They wouldn't dare risk him again. It's a pity, really, because I suppose we will have to get to know the next chap they appoint! Perhaps you could make use of Zonakas.'

Fletcher didn't answer straight away. His feelings towards Zonakas were less friendly than Spencer's. Zonakas had been prepared to send Mario and himself to a watery grave. Fletcher wouldn't forget that in a hurry, and he shuddered to think what would happen if Zonakas and Mario came face to face.

'I don't think that would be very practicable,' he said quietly.

'Only a thought,' Spencer said. 'Got to make use of anyone these days.'

Fletcher changed the subject.

'It looks as if we are the only ones who have come out of it unscathed. I don't think the Communists are going to be too pleased with Veti.'

'I'll reserve my judgment until I have seen a report on the cargo Rassitz was carrying. It's my hunch that it's a lot of hogwash. The Russians may have invented this form of roulette, but they stopped playing it a long time ago, so have the Albanians. Either Veti was building up his own nest egg or the Albanian treasury received an inflated payment for something they didn't want.'

'What about the technicians?'

'Very impressive,' Spencer agreed, 'and very convincing, but I bet they would have vanished into thin air the moment they landed on Cyprus.'

'Maybe, maybe not.' Fletcher muttered. Spencer was a sceptic and a diplomat. He saw everything as a move and a counter-move, a threat and a bluff, but Fletcher didn't go along with him all the way. Fletcher worked on the ground, in the thick of the danger. Rassitz was real enough, so was Ikarios, and so was Veti. No, he felt certain the Communists had tried to stir it up on Cyprus. Veti certainly wouldn't risk doing a private deal. Fletcher knew the way the K.G.B. worked as well as his own organisation. Veti would have never lived to spend the money.

'I think you will find a boat load of very valuable guided missiles, made in Hungary or Czechoslovakia, and a further stock pile in Durres waiting to be picked up,' he said quietly.

Spencer was slightly taken aback by Fletcher's serious tone.

'You may be correct, Fletcher,' he said, 'but you are not implying that the Communists instigated the whole thing, are you?'

'No,' Fletcher said. 'They came in the side door. Zonakas thought it all up. Pula was his go between. I think if you check back on him you'll find he has worked for the Communists before. But the Communists don't like being used, and when they found out he was double dealing them, they killed him and dealt direct with Rassitz. If they hadn't been so interested they would have pulled out. The fact that they stayed in the game makes me think they were heavily committed.'

'You have a point there,' Spencer agreed rather begrudingly. 'Very fortunate for Rassitz.'

'Yes, but Rassitz suspected the Greeks and wasn't unduly worried where the goods came from.'

Spencer sighed.

'Well, it is all over now. I think I might even take a few days off and get away from this damned heat. By the way,' he added, 'who was that priest who delivered your message?'

'What priest?' Fletcher asked seriously, 'I don't know any priests.'

Spencer saw the stubborn look on Fletcher's face and knew he wasn't going to get anything out of him.

'Never mind,' he said. 'I was probably mistaken.'

Fletcher purposely let the matter pass, and cast a last glance at the two destroyers, and wondered what Salunda was thinking.

As they walked away from the rails, Mario joined them. He looked at the open sea.

'Has it gone?' he asked.

'Yes,' Spencer muttered, 'about ten minutes ago.'

Mario frowned.

'You know you could have saved that yacht if you had come at full speed,' he said seriously.

'Yes, I agree,' Spencer said, 'but...' He paused and looked at Fletcher, but Fletcher had gone. He was on his own. 'Yes, I agree,' he said, resigned to another long discussion, 'but it saves a lot of embarrassment this way...'

Fletcher lay on his bunk and through a porthole watched an ocean liner nose its way slowly into the harbour. It was four days since they had been picked up by Spencer and taken to Serifos to collect their boat. The diplomatic world of the Balkans had restored its equilibrium and was at peace. Spencer had gone off to the mountains for a few days' rest, and the Ambassador was tying up the final details for the conference.

Fletcher's world was also quiet. The heat at the height of the summer discouraged a brisk underworld of activity. But if his business activities were peaceful, Fletcher himself was very restless. After the excitement, the calm was an anticlimax. For three days they had remained in the crowded Piraeus harbour. After the first taste of a life ashore, the novelty became a bore. The hotels looked even more shabby than before, the bars more sleazy, and the girls less attractive. Mario was itching to be off, anywhere, so long as they were on the move, but Fletcher was reluctant to leave. He wouldn't give a reason for wanting to stay and wouldn't even confess to himself that he had one. All he would promise was that they would leave after a few days.

He lit a cigarette and contemplated leaving his bunk to watch the visitors disembark, but talked himself out of it. He heard footsteps pad across the deck and was surprised that Mario had returned so soon. But the steps were not Mario's! Instantly he became alert. He knew Mario's steps, these were not his, they were too gentle. In a flash he was off his bunk. He didn't like visitors; it usually meant trouble. He crossed over to the steps leading to the deck and met his visitor full on – it was Salunda!

'You!' he gasped.

She smiled. The provocative, teasing smile she had shown the last time she had been on his boat. Fletcher continued to gape. It was a different Salunda from the one he had known before. Her black hair hung loosely on her shoulders; her face looked happy, free from any strain or fears. She was wearing a colourful dress which matched her mood and accentuated the curves of her body. In her hand was a small grip bag.

'Surprised?' she asked.

Fletcher gave his usual nervous cough and dropped his eyes.

'Well, yes,' he mumbled in his deep gravel voice. He quickly got over his embarrassment. 'Come in,' he said, and stood to one side.

She entered the cabin and sat on one of the bunks.

'I have come to thank you,' she said.

Fletcher sat opposite her and admitted to himself the real reason why he had been reluctant to leave Piraeus. He had been secretly hoping she would return. It had seemed very unlikely, but whilst there had been only the slimmest of possibilities he hadn't wanted to give up.

'Sorry,' he said apologetically. 'What did you say?'

She smiled at him.

'I have come to thank you,' she said again, 'and the British Government.'

Fletcher coughed and looked away.

'Well, I can't speak for the British Government,' he said hastily, 'I have no idea how they became involved.'

'But they are very much involved,' she persisted. 'Not only did they send their navy to stop Rassitz, but they have also smoothed out all the troubles at the diplomatic level.'

'Have they by jove,' Fletcher muttered.

She gave him a look of mock horror.

'Don't you know, Stefan?' she asked.

Fletcher looked at her and realised she was teasing him. She started to laugh, and Fletcher joined her.

'Seriously, Stefan,' she said, 'my father and I do thank you.'

'Who is your father?' Fletcher asked.

'Dr Mohmad Izmad,' she said.

'Deputy leader of the Turkish Cypriots?' Fletcher asked.

'Yes,' Salunda said, and added sadly: 'If only they had listened to him at the very beginning it would have saved a lot of trouble.'

'Why didn't they?' Fletcher asked.

'Rassitz had friends in Cyprus and Turkey. Powerful friends.' She shrugged. 'It is the way of the world. If you talk peace, you are a weakling. If you talk of war and fighting, you are a brave, strong man. So they listened to Rassitz and not my father. Now at the conference they will have to listen to my father and our leader. There is no Rassitz.'

'So you came along to protect your father's interests?' Fletcher asked.

She gave a rueful smile.

'It rather looked that way,' she said. 'The Turkish Ambassador in Athens is a distant relation of my mother's. We persuaded my father to let us come to Athens to watch developments. I can be very persuasive and my father finally agreed.' She dropped her eyes. 'Also Kasim wanted to prove himself to my father. He believed in my father. I think it was only because of Kasim that my father permitted us to come. When we arrived here, we engaged Kronos to go to Serifos to see if anything suspicious developed.'

'And the name Lofer?' Fletcher asked.

'That was the code name given to the operation by the Turks. We also used it. It is short for Loferbraun.'

'Yes, I know. Did Kronos find anything.'

'He came across Dr Sleitser and learned about the secret mine-shaft down to the cave. It was used by the Germans during the war.'

'That was all?' Fletcher asked.

'That was all he told us,' Salunda said. 'We got a message from him saying he had something important to tell us, but what it was we never found out. He never turned up at the meeting we arranged.'

No, thought Fletcher, because Zonakas had got to him first and bribed him to keep quiet. But when Fletcher had appeared on the scene, they couldn't trust him to remain silent so they had killed him.

'Then you turned up,' Salunda added.

'So you used me as bait,' Fletcher said with a smile.

She looked embarrassed.

'That was Rassitz' idea. He was in command then. It was important that I didn't upset him at that stage. Kasim didn't agree, and he went on his own to see what he could find.'

'What did he expect to find?' Fletcher asked.

She made a despairing gesture.

'Anything, nothing,' she said. 'Kasim thought the Greeks, or the Communists, were instigating the whole plot. He thought they would have some of their men in the town or watching Sleitser's camp. He hoped to bring back proof that would make Rassitz return to Turkey.'

'Instead he met some of Rassitz' men and they killed him,' Fletcher said sadly.

'Yes,' Salunda agreed, 'but I didn't learn this until it was too late, or I would have avenged Kasim myself.'

'Rassitz is dead,' Fletcher said. 'He can do no more harm.'

'Yes, he is dead,' she muttered and then looked up brightly. 'And what are your plans, Stefan? Where do you go to now?'

He hesitated before replying. He knew what he would like to do. He would like to take the *Tonos* and Salunda away from

Piraeus, away from heat and crowds. Away to one of Mario's idyllic islands, where they could be alone together. He looked at her and their eyes met. There was an appealing look on her face. He felt a tightening in his throat. Could she possibly be feeling the same way? Was that why she had returned? He found himself moving over to her. She stood up to meet him.

'I know what I would like to do,' he whispered hoarsely.

'Tell me,' she pleaded.

'Later,' he said quietly and took her in his arms...

In a small bar overlooking the harbour, Mario gave a sudden cry of delight. He stood up, abruptly, and the girl who had been sitting on his knee fell ungracefully to the floor.

'Ho! Ho!' he chuckled, a broad grin on his face.

'Well!' the girl snapped. 'You might have warned me.'

Mario ignored her and gazed across the harbour to where he could see the *Tonos* moving slowly away from its moorings. He gave another chuckle. He had seen Salunda go aboard and had waited the outcome with interest. Now he had got his answer.

He grabbed the girl and smacked her playfully.

'Get another bottle,' he said jubilantly. 'We are going to celebrate.'

'Celebrate?' the girl asked. 'Celebrate what?'

'My farewell,' he said secretively.

'Your farewell?' she asked. 'Where are you going?'

'Never mind,' he chuckled. 'Fetch the bottle.'

The girl did as she was told, but when she returned Mario had gone. In his place was a ten drachma note. She picked up the note and shrugged. She wasn't interested in Mario any more. Nor was he with her. He was more concerned about catching the ferry which was preparing to leave the harbour.

The publishers hope that this book has given you enjoyable reading. Large Print Books are especially designed to be as easy to see and hold as possible. If you wish a complete list of our books please ask at your local library or write directly to:

Magna Large Print Books
Magna House, Long Preston,
Skipton, North Yorkshire.
BD23 4ND

This Large Print Book, for people
who cannot read normal print,
is published under the auspices of

THE ULVERSCROFT FOUNDATION

... we hope you have enjoyed this book.
Please think for a moment about those
who have worse eyesight than you ...
and are unable to even read or enjoy
Large Print without great difficulty.

You can help them by sending a
donation, large or small, to:

**The Ulverscroft Foundation,
1, The Green, Bradgate Road,
Anstey, Leicestershire, LE7 7FU,
England.**
or request a copy of our brochure for
more details.

The Foundation will use all donations
to assist those people who are visually
impaired and need special attention
with medical research, diagnosis
and treatment.

Thank you very much for your help.